Eric Fèvre

Psychic disability

Data subjects, events, processing operations, a definition and an evaluation grid

ScienciaScripts

Imprint

Cover image: www.ingimage.com

This book is a translation from the original published under ISBN 978-3-8381-4596-9.

Publisher:
Sciencia Scripts
is a trademark of
International Book Market Service Ltd., member of OmniScriptum Publishing Group
17 Meldrum Street, Beau Bassin 71504, Mauritius
Printed at: see last page
ISBN: 978-620-0-89305-5

Éric FÈVRE

Psychic disability

The Situation of Psychic Disability (SHOP) : a French folly. The people concerned, the SHOP events, a definition, an evaluation grid.

Introduction

Although the term "disability" is a recent term, people with disabilities have always existed. At least some have been noticed.
However, before the appearance of the signifier "handicap" in the 16th century, the differences of some humans were not well identified. Until very recently, the words were used indiscriminately: crippled, invalid, impotent, mutilated, wounded, amputee, crippled, paralytic, crippled, crippled, lame, disgraced, retarded, atrophied, incapable, ignorant, imbecile, idiot, dumb, sick, suffering, handicapped, handicapped, stupid, bewildered, dumb, lame, wobbly, degenerate, mad, insane, clubfoot, insane, insane, irresponsible, insane, madman, hallucinated, and so on. Neither was a distinction always made between disability and illness; the treatments of the two were very similar, they took into account the understanding of the medicine of the place and time, and more often than not made no distinction between body and mind (Sendrail, 1980).

For my part, in my home town of Lorient, in the 1970s, we used to joke about the "débiles de Kerpape", named after a famous functional re-education centre (CRF) located nearby: we then blithely confused intellectual disability with physical disability (BMI in[1] particular); and we didn't go swimming on the beach at Kerpape, to avoid being contaminated, probably for fear of poliomyelitis. Similarly, in my childhood, in primary school, students in advanced classes were booed, called "grignous" - the Lorient term for tramps, the homeless[2] - children then assimilated their academic backwardness and a future adult social decline. More recently, in the 1980s, an autistic teenage girl on a Parisian bus sat in a seat coveted by an old lady, who at first offended and then excused herself: "I didn't see that you were crippled"; an outdated term referring to a physical deformity, an interpretation of the bodily manifestation of autism.

The debate continues today, around a recent notion: psychic disability. Just as the ancient Greeks wondered whether madness was a medical or philosophical issue, the question arises as to the origin of mental handicap: is it due to a mental illness (psychiatric point of view) or does it come from a psychological fragility (opinion of certain medical-social teams). The question is not insignificant: depending on the point of view, the approach, the conception of the situation, one will take care of a patient, help a patient, accompany a user, or even offer a service to a client.

---

[1] Cerebral Palsy is a term used today to describe a cerebral palsy.
[2] Homeless

Concerning myself, in the background, in the fundamental debate, because of my Lacanian culture, the question of a differential diagnosis will always arise: from a structural point of view, in each case, is it a question of neurosis, psychosis, perversion, or even autism?
The 1975 *Disability* Act allowed the term to become established and quickly replaced the terms "disabled" and "maladjusted". (Chapireau; Constant; Durand, 1997). Today, disability can be approached in different ways and from different perspectives. We usually encounter four approaches: functional, social, environmental individualistic and biomedical.

- The *functional* approach is read in a public policy context, it includes the procedures and means put in place in favour of persons with disabilities as a category of citizens.
- The *social* approach takes place at a point in history and describes disability as a product of the cultural representations of an era.
- The *individualistic environmental* approach takes into account the material environment (the places) and the human environment (the entourage) of the disabled person.
- The *biomedical* approach focuses on the nature and severity of the disability, as well as personal factors (such as age, for example).
- But neither could we ignore *historical*, *cultural*, *economic* approaches.

The Disability Act 2005 has allowed for the recognition of *mental disability*.

In France, since 1997, *boarding houses* - or *maison relais* - have been taking in vulnerable people. In 2006, a new form of boarding house was created for elderly people or people suffering from mental disabilities, called *Résidence Accueil*. These are social structures, financed by the State from the Social Cohesion budget. For example, a *Residence* can accommodate a person who leaves the psychiatric hospital after a mental illness to be housed in an independent apartment in the residence as a mentally *handicapped* person; but, since it is financed by the State and not by health insurance, it does not have to obtain the status of handicapped person issued by any authority: mentally handicapped, of course, but without official recognition.
In addition, a *Residence* also receives mentally handicapped persons who have never had a psychiatric career, who have never been diagnosed as mentally ill, who have never received treatment for any mental illness; and yet, in order to be received there, they must be *mentally handicapped,* recognized as such by the admissions commission of the establishment, in the absence of any medical certificate. Thus, for example, the admissions committee of the reception residence of the association that I directed was composed of the director, a state representative (DDCS inspector[3]), a representative of the department ([4]FSL service), and a

---

[3] Departmental Directorate of Social Cohesion

representative of the HLM office[5] that had built the residence: no competence expected in psychopathology. The files were presented by the two hosts of the residence who had taken their information from the social workers who had presented the candidates.

Similarly, in the city, there are *Mutual Assistance Groups* (GEM), associations under the 1901 law, which bring together people with mental disabilities, and which are financed by the Regional Health Agency (ARS); access is open to any person who recognizes himself as being mentally *handicapped* and recognized by others as being able to benefit from this system; no medical certificate or certificate of disability is required. In the three GEMs managed by the association that I directed, the admission was pronounced by the GEM office, composed of members elected among the supposedly psychically handicapped members, after a trial period of one month, because the behaviour of the candidate was in conformity with that usually expected.

Thus, we note that two devices, financed by French public authorities, receive people recognized as *mentally handicapped* outside of any medical diagnosis. We thus see an original conception of mental *disability*: alongside that of a part of psychiatry for which mental disability is the consequence and continuation of a psychiatric condition, there is another one according to which a person can be in a situation of mental disability without there being an underlying mental illness. That is why I support a broader concept of mental disability than the narrower one that is advocated by a large part of psychiatry and also of the medical and social sector, and which may even include it: mental disability as a result of mental illness is a specific mental disability.

I am going to present you my vision of this French particularity which is - what we will call later - the "situation of handicap of psychic origin" and which concerns both psychotic and neurotic people.
There is, of course, a link between madness and psychic handicap, but we shall see what it is, and we shall know how to put it into perspective. "Disability refers to limitations in activity and restrictions in the social participation of people due to health problems, impairments or illnesses. What has just been stated is not the common vision of disability, particularly in France; this viewpoint is not widely shared. However, no disability specialist will reject it.
On the other hand, with regard to mental disability, there is no consensual vision such as one could give here a definition that brings together all points of view; the question of knowing, for example, what is the relationship between mental disability and mental illness would

---

4 Housing Solidarity Fund
5 Low-rent housing

immediately be debated. Beyond a semantic question, it is indeed about representations. But behind these representations, there are suffering people who need care.

It seems necessary to me that, in a first chapter, we should be able to circumscribe the field of disability in general. To do so, we will have to go through this field, in all directions, to know its contents and outlines. We will therefore first of all look for what is covered by the meaning of "handicap".

In a second chapter, we will try to clarify what a "psychic handicap" can be and see also its related, neighbouring fields, such as those of mental health and mental illness.

In a third and final chapter, we will attempt to construct a clinical picture of psychological disability, and then to produce an evaluation grid of the situation of disability of psychological origin that could be used by specialized teams. Finally, we will hypothesize a syndrome at the origin of the psychological handicap.

The book is divided into the following parts:

1. Disabilities: in this first part, we will discuss the concept of disability. We will use history to see the appearance of this signifier in its different meanings, in the world, in Europe, and then in France; we will focus more particularly on the period from 1945 to 2017. We will have to study institutional functioning in order to grasp the complexity of the field of disability in which some people with disabilities are struggling. Through a quick historical review of the consideration of the disabled in France from the High Middle Ages onwards, and among them the so-called "poor in spirit", we will see the progressive implementation of institutional measures to help them, particularly from the Second World War onwards.
We will see the meaning of "handicap" in its different meanings and how this notion is approached in the world, then in Europe and more particularly in France since 1945. In addition to the legislative aspect, it is on the institutions and their functioning that I am going to focus, my concern being to show, in the end, the complexity of the societal context and the difficulties that may result for people with mental disabilities.

2. The psychic handicap: in the second part, we will study this singular category of handicap which is the psychic handicap. This recent notion seems to be a French specificity. We will see its emergence in the second half of the 20th century, and its recognition at the beginning of the 21st century.
We will also discover the bodies that take it into account, with their own approach. We will note the proximity of this handicap and mental illness, which we will question from a historical point of view and based on the conceptions of the actors in these related fields.
We will examine recent definitions of psychiatric disability that do not refer to an assumed underlying mental illness. I will then be led to produce a definition of mental disability that could be consensual.

3. Clinic of the psychic handicap: in this third part, we will characterize the psychic handicap, by relying on writings; we will try to update all the characteristics of the situation of handicap of psychic origin. We will thus characterize psychic handicap in France from a clinical point of view. Starting from the different representations of this singular handicap, we will produce a clinical picture of psychic handicap.
Then we will present an evaluation grid of the situation of handicap of psychic origin.
We will conclude by indicating, upstream of the situation of disability of psychic origin, a discrete incapacitating syndrome that could be diagnosed by specialized multi-professional teams.

1. Disabilities

In this first part, we will begin by addressing the historical aspect of the emergence of the notion of disability in France.
This part consists of the following chapters:

1.1 **Taking disabilities into account**: this historical section will give a very broad picture of the concept of disability.

1.2 **Disability**: we will examine the concept of disability in order to clarify it, and we will study the bodies that have been set up to circumscribe it.

1.3 **Vulnerable persons**: we will study measures to protect persons with disabilities.

1.4 **The Disability Production Process**: we will discuss this Quebec concept and see its interest.

1.1 Taking account of disabilities

In this first chapter, we will quickly go back to the origins of the concept of disability. We are not going to repeat the numerous works on this subject; we will try to present quickly our point of view on the issue, from the point of view of a social worker turned pedagogue and clinician.

During the High Middle Ages, the first "Hotels God" were built to welcome the poor, whether they were infirm, old or poor, indiscriminately. From the 14th century onwards, this charitable attitude gave way to fear; this population of poor people, of beggars, was put aside. Among the cripples, the "poor in spirit" were the first to be locked up; thus, at the end of the 17th century, they were welcomed in Paris at the General Hospital *La Salpêtrière*.
In 1674, the Institution des Invalides was created by Louis XIV to take in veterans of his wars who were no longer able to work. Order reigned there according to a system that was both military and religious. The most able-bodied participate in its functioning, among other things by working in shoemaking, tapestry and illumination workshops. Under the Consulate, then under the Empire, Napoleon Bonaparte restructured the institution.
Sensory deficiencies were taken into account in the Enlightenment, under the influence of scientific advances and new philosophical theories.

Deaf and blind people were the first to be helped by educationalists.
In the 13th century Saint Bonaventure created a manual alphabet for teaching the sounds of spoken language, letter by letter, from which the current French dactylology derives.
In the sixteenth century, Pedro Ponce de Leon, a Spanish Benedictine monk, worked to educate some deaf children from the nobility.
In 1620, Juan Pablo Bonet, a Spanish pedagogue, published a work entitled: *Simplification of the letters of the alphabet and teaching method allowing the deaf to speak,* based on the works

of Saint Bonaventure. Also in the 17th century, John Wallis, an English mathematician, was the precursor of phonetics, education of the deaf and speech therapy. He left a treatise on phonetics: *De Loquela.* Johann Conrad Amman, a doctor born in Switzerland and based in Amsterdam, was one of the first to stress the importance of lip reading for the deaf.
In the 18th century, Samuel Heinicke, a German schoolteacher, founded the first public institution for the education of the deaf and dumb in Leipzig in 1778. Jacob-Rodrigues Pereire, a Spanish teacher who had taken refuge in France, was a tutor of deaf children; he developed dactylology based on the method of Saint Bonaventure used by Bonet. The Abbé de l'Épée, creator in 1760 of the first private school for the deaf and dumb, invented the Langue des Signes Française (LSF).
Valentin Haüy founded the first free school for blind boys and girls in Paris in 1786.
In 1749, Denis Diderot published his "Lettre sur les aveugles à l'usage de ceux qui voient". In 1790, the Begging Committee, chaired by La Rochefoucault-Liancourt, asserted before the Constituent Assembly the Nation's duty to assist the needy.

In France, from the middle of the 13th century until the 19th century, children and the elderly were, by right, exempt from working, as well as often women and the infirm; they were then subject to charitable assistance. While able-bodied men and beggars were forced to work, the infirm were excluded by right; not only were they exempt, but they were excluded (Castel, 1995). And not only were they excluded from work, but sometimes from society in general (Stiker, 2009).
However, specialized institutions are created for deaf and blind children and adults, with specific technological development to compensate for their communication difficulties, such as Sign Language and Braille Alphabet.

In the 19th century, interest was focused on "idiot" children: Jean Itard, a pioneering doctor in otorhinolaryngology, was interested in the case of young Victor de l'Aveyron, a young "savage"; if, like the alienist Philippe Pinel, he noticed the child's idiocy, he did not think it was irreversible; for Victor, relying on Rousseau's pedagogical principles of modifying his environment, he invented a method of awakening his senses.
Édouard Séguin is at the origin of the education of intellectually deficient children; in 1837, he begins the education of a young "idiot", according to the nosography of the time; his work is noticed by the alienist Esquirol; Séguin later directs a school at the hospital of Bicêtre and he invents there a "medico-educational" method. He is convinced that no child is "ineducable"; he invents the educational material that will allow each child to progress. Bourneville created the first psychiatric service at Bicêtre exclusively reserved for "retarded" and "idiot" children; he applied the Séguin method. In 1900, he received a visit from Maria Montessori who, taking up the work of Itard and Séguin, invented his method intended first for handicapped children, then for all children (Fèvre, 2011).

Bourneville took an active part in the vote on Alfred Binet's law in 1909 instituting advanced training classes.

In 1889, a congress of the Assistancy drew up an assistance charter in Paris. In the following years, several laws on assistance were passed.
After long and conflictual discussions in the last decades of the 19th century, France passed a law on accidents at work in 1898; it made the employer responsible for a specific insurance policy allowing the payment of compensation for disabilities acquired in the course of work. The fact that "citizens damaged by work" were very numerous made it possible to develop the concept of "social responsibility", and thus "social solidarity". It is no longer nature, it is no longer chance, it is no longer war that produces infirmity, but a social fact - work - that changes society in its representations (Sticker, 2009).
In 1905 the law on assistance to the elderly, infirm and incurable was passed. In the same year, another law created the classes of improvement; annexed to the elementary schools, they take in "backward" children.

While the notion of disability first progressed in France from that of "compensation" for work-related accidents, the issue was also addressed after the 1914-1918 war by the question of getting "war-disabled" back to work. Thus, the "war invalids", but also the "great civilian invalids", acquired rights when they could no longer work: a replacement income - this invalidity pension, which is still current - is the result of a long struggle waged in parallel by the veterans and the workers' unions. In 1916, laws were enacted to reserve jobs for the disabled victims of the First World War. A law of 1918 created the National Office for the Disabled and Reformed of War, which subsidized rehabilitation schools. In 1919, the Department of Veterans Affairs introduced a disability assessment scale for war victims to determine the amount of their disability pension. A 1924 law made it mandatory for companies to recruit military personnel receiving a disability pension. In 1930, a law gave the right to victims of industrial accidents to be admitted free of charge to the vocational rehabilitation schools that were set up by the military for the disabled of the First World War.
During the Second World War, the British, in the context of the war effort to bring together all production capacities, developed a doctrine which led to what they called *rehabilitation* - and which could be translated into French as "réadaptation", if this term did not have a traditional meaning linked to physical disability -; this rehabilitation which consists of techniques for access to civic life, particularly to work. We will find these notions later on.
In France, the Social Security system was created in 1945 to insure all employees against the consequences of non-work-related illnesses and accidents that deprive them of their "earning capacity". In 1946, France adopted a new Constitution. In its preamble, it is written that any person who is unable to work, including because of "his physical or mental condition", must be

financially assisted. A law of 1949 creates a Compensation Allowance for Greatly Disabled Workers and gives them access to vocational training.
A decree of 1953 created the departmental guidance commissions for the disabled for the recognition of fitness for work or access to vocational rehabilitation. A decree of 1954 creates the Centres d'aide par le travail (C.A.T.), enterprises which receive financial assistance from the State to employ disabled workers in order to give them access to employment; they concern all types of disability.
The terms used until then (*infirm, diminished, incurable, invalid, mutilated, impotent, dumb,* etc.) stemmed from a propensity to want to categorize people; this categorization is based on personal imperfections; it is based on initial judgments about different people on whom stereotyped attributes are placed. Some of the terms used evoke a definitive and fixed situation. Progress in medicine and technology, as well as changes in care facilities, will open up wider prospects for the development and change of people with Alzheimer's disease in their bodies and even in their minds. It is this variability of situations that will allow the term "handicap" to come into its own.

Nowadays, there are many handicaps: physical (motor impairments, cerebral palsy, myopathy, lesional affections), sensory (visual, auditory), mental, psychic, as consequences of serious and disabling illnesses, and there is even an aesthetic handicap; we also find the polyhandicap (association of severe motor and intellectual deficiencies), the multihandicap (or multihandicap, association of several deficiencies) and the overhandicap (aggravation of a handicap due to relational problems caused by the handicap). It is even sometimes referred to as social disability.
Different organizations advocate or represent people with disabilities. Among them, among the first to emerge are the following: the National Federation of Industrial Accidents (today FNATH), created in 1921; LADAPT, created in 1929 by a person with tuberculosis who was shocked by the confinement and idleness of sick people; the Association des paralysés de France (APF), created in 1933 by three young men and one young woman suffering from poliomyelitis and revolted against the exclusion of which they were victims; the Papillons Blancs, created in 1948 by families of mentally handicapped people; the Association d'Aide au Placement des Adolescents Handicapés (now APAJH) created in 1962 to take in handicapped young people who had no place in the National Education system.
Since then, many associations have been created, grouped together and spread, whether they are the offspring of disabled people themselves, relatives or citizens who are aware of their cause. Many are specialized in a particular disability.

In this first section, a picture of disability in the broadest sense has been painted. We will now be able to go into the details of the notion of disability.

1.2 Disability

In this second section, we will focus more on the concept of disability itself. In addition to the linguistic and historical aspects, we will try to see the emergence of different ways of understanding and conceiving the concept of disability. We will learn about the work of international bodies, European institutions and the French State. We will then study in detail the bodies set up by the law of February 2005 on disability.
I have chosen to end this chapter with this law of 2005, in order, in the next chapter, to go into more detail in this law as far as mental disability is concerned. This choice thus leads me to present this research from the international to the national level. Moreover, in the 21st century, most French laws are variations of European directives.

The word "handicap" is used in France, in everyday discourse, in different contexts and with different meanings: "it is more difficult to find work when you are disabled", "being black is a handicap in looking for work", "bad polls are a handicap in the race for elections", etc. In the specialized circles of the medico-social sector, it is encountered in several forms: "a person with a disability, a carrier of a disability, in a situation of disability, the day of the disability, overcoming the disability, compensating for the disability, mental handicap" and in other grammatical forms: "handicapped, handicapping, handicapping" and even "handicapologist".

Originally, the word "handicap" was derived from the English language, a contraction of the three words "hand i' cap", or "hand in (the) cap". (Rossignol, 2002). It appeared in Great Britain in the sixteenth century to designate a game with an element of chance. A person offers to put into play a good belonging to another and exchange it with one of his own; they choose a referee. The three comrades decide on a sum to compensate for the difference in value, and each puts a hand containing the decided amount in his hat. At a given moment, each one removes his hand from his hat; depending on whether the hands are full (of the amount bet) or empty, the conditions of the exchange are fixed.
From this origin, we will retain the idea that the handicap may consist in a compensation of a lesser value of an exchanged object, or in the restoration of equality in an exchange; the terms "compensation" and "restoration" will be used in the course of our research.
At the end of the 17th century, the term "handicap" was applied to the organisation of challenges between two horses with unequal performances. In the 18th century, the expression "Handy-Cap Match" appeared. In the nineteenth century, the verbal form "handicap" is attested in English to refer to the action of "weighing down, hindering, or in any way penalizing a superior competitor so as to reduce his chances in favor of inferior competitors", then more generally "putting someone at a disadvantage by the imposition of some hindrance, obstacle or incapacity", and finally in a metaphorical way as in "he is handicapped by the weight of his reputation" or "the weight of public expenditure handicaps the country". Note, in this second

appearance of the signifier "handicap", that it is an action aimed at restoring a certain balance by restoring the chances of those who are disadvantaged; we will find later this idea of the same right for all to access chances of success. We will also see that the meaning of "disability" will evolve to become a kind of burden that reduces opportunities, which will have to be compensated for, in the idea of an equalization of opportunities. Let us remember, however, that handicap consists, here, of a load that an animal carries, a load that hinders it and that does not allow it to reach its best performance. While the idea of this additional burden is easily understandable in the case of a physically disabled person, we find this notion in the expression used in particular by parents of mentally disabled persons: a child "carrying a disability", which makes it possible to imagine a less visible disability.

In France, in the 19th century, the term "handicap" corresponds to a specific terminology of horse racing.

> *"A handicap race is a race open to horses whose chances of winning are naturally unequal, and are, in principle, equalized by the obligation on the best horse to carry a greater weight"* (Bryon, 1827).

Disability therefore meant, then, to equalize opportunities, by an artifice that mitigates natural inequalities. This notion of equalization of opportunities will be very present at the beginning of the 21st century. It was not until 1930 that the term "disability" was used to designate a social disadvantage or a physical defect (Stiker, 1996). In 1940, the dictionary Le Robert introduced the term "physical handicap". The positive connotation of the original meaning is transformed into a disadvantage that a person experiences in competition with others. Little by little, this figurative meaning came to the fore; for example, "a person has been handicapped as a result of an accident".

Returning to the English language, disability can be translated as *impairment,* in reference to impairments that may give rise to social rights, but also as *disability* that is used in activist circles in an egalitarian claim (Weber, 2016). The English language uses *disability to refer to* the consequences on daily life of a medical impairment or chronic illness.

We are going to take a step back to observe this notion of disability, by making the empirical choice to start from a global vision, to tighten our approach on a European scale and to come to a French conception which will remain the field of our research. Indeed, I believe that the French context is part of world history, even if we will see that some concepts take, for example, several decades to cross the Atlantic Ocean. We will thus approach the official texts of world bodies: a look at disability in France can only take into account, for example, the work of the World Health Organization (WHO) from the moment it takes an interest in the subject. Then, considering that a very large part of French laws are applications of European directives, we will look at the work of European bodies.

1.2.1 Global institutions and disability

In this section, we will now look at the work on disability of two international bodies: the United Nations Organization (UN) - created in 1945, bringing together almost all the states of the world - and the World Health Organization - created in 1948, which is a specialized agency of the UN. For greater readability, the texts will be grouped by decades.

In 1975, the UN wrote and adopted the *Declaration on the Rights of Disabled Persons*.

In 1980, the WHO drafted the *International Classification of impairments, disabilities and handicaps* (ICIDH), a text in English in which the term *disability* appears only at the third level, when a person encounters external obstacles in his or her environment that hinder or even prevent him or her from running (Stiker, 2009). This text is only approved on an experimental basis. The year 1981 was declared by the United Nations as the International Year of Disabled Persons. On this occasion, the United Nations headquarters in New York and the United Nations Offices in Geneva and Vienna were made accessible to people with reduced mobility (PRM). AT the end of 1981, three international events are held, bringing together experts in the field of disability, technical assistance for the prevention of disability and the rehabilitation of disabled persons, as well as initiatives and strategies concerning education, prevention of disability and integration of disabled persons in cooperation with UNESCO, the United Nations Educational, Scientific and Cultural Organization (UNESCO, 2015). In 1982, the United Nations General Assembly adopted its World Plan of Action for Disabled Persons: it is structured around three main areas: *prevention*, *rehabilitation* and *equalization of opportunities*. The General Assembly proclaims the decade 1983-1992 as the United Nations Decade of *Disabled Persons, with the* aim of providing a time frame for organizations to carry out the activities recommended in its Programme of Action. In 1983, the Secretary-General of the United Nations announces the publication of a report on action to prevent disability. In writing what was to become a world programme, the UN involved people with disabilities as experts. In its article 3, the programme defines disability: it includes the meanings of "environment", "barriers" and "participation". In 1989, the UN General Assembly adopted the *Tallinn Principles* for Action on Human Resources Development in the Field of Disability, which set out the means of action to promote the participation, training and employment of persons with disabilities.

In the 1990s, five world conferences were held under the aegis of the United Nations. The work emphasised the need to create a society for all, with the participation of all citizens, including people with disabilities, in all sectors of society. The 1991 General Assembly adopts *Principles for the Protection and Improvement of the Care of the Mentally Ill*. The definition

of the freedoms and rights of persons with mental disabilities is based on twenty-five fundamental principles.
The *Standard Rules on the Equalization of Opportunities for Persons with Disabilities were* adopted in 1993 by the United Nations and[6] consist of 22 rules. The 1994 International Conference on Population and Development calls upon States to ensure that persons with disabilities enjoy their rights and participate in all aspects of social, economic and cultural life; it calls for the strengthening of conditions for the equalization of opportunities for persons with disabilities and the recognition of their capabilities in economic and social life; it requires the assurance of respect for their dignity and the promotion of their independence.

The WHO adopted the *International Classification of Functioning* (ICF) in 2001[7]. This so-called "functioning" classification describes a person's disability situation through the interaction between his or her characteristics and those of his or her environment. It highlights the disabilities and disadvantages of people with disabilities. Disabilities concern behaviour, communication, locomotion, handling, body care, use of the body in certain tasks and situations. Disadvantages relate to physical independence, mobility, occupations, schooling, work, economic independence and social integration. In the genesis of disability, ICF focuses on the person's life situations, which constitutes a kind of compromise between the three usual currents of conception of disability: the medical current (pathology and consequences), the Woodian current (incapacity, disadvantage), and the "socio-environmentalist" current (obstacles). ICF is constructed from the records of the existence of the human person, of his or her mind and body - and therefore of his or her organs and their functions -, of social activities - from the most elementary to the most cultural -, and of his or her more or less developed participation in society. The factors that limit the person's being and participation are those related to the person himself, those of his environment and those resulting from pathologies due to illness or accidents. From the introduction, the text recalls - among other things - the role that the environment can play in the onset of disability: disability is seen as being mainly the consequence of a complex set of situations, many of which are created by the social environment. Disability is conceived as a problem created by society, to be understood as a question of integration of people in society. Although the ICF seeks to describe disability within a universal and non-discriminatory model of human functioning - including the use of neutral language - Stiker (2009) notes that the activities described in the ICF correspond to a relatively conformist Western model, where notions of conflict or revolt are erased. The universe described is behaviourist, with people without psyches, almost standardized, even computerized: we see in them neither desires, nor hatred, nor fantasies, nor perversity.

---

[6] http://www.un.org/french/esa/social/disabled/PDF/ReglesEgalisationChances.pdf
[7] http://www.who.int/classifications/icf/en/

In 2006, the UN adopted the *Convention on the Rights of Persons with Disabilities* (CRPD)[8]. Its purpose is to guarantee, promote and protect the equal rights and all fundamental freedoms of persons with disabilities, and also to call for respect for their dignity. It reflects a major shift in the global understanding of and response to disability. Indeed, it gives persons with disabilities the same rights as others. In its preamble, and then in article 12, it states that every person has rights, freedoms, duties, a place and a role in society. Thus, all persons with disabilities have the same rights: they therefore have legal capacity in all areas and must be provided, if necessary, with support in the form of decision-making aids, human assistance or technical aids. This convention will only be adopted by France in March 2010. In 2011, however, there are 147 signatory countries and 99 ratifications obtained.

In 2011, the WHO publishes its definition of disability:

> *"Disabled persons are those whose physical or mental integrity is progressively or permanently diminished, either congenitally or as a result of age, illness or accident, to such an extent that their independence, ability to attend school or to hold a job is impaired".*[9]

This approach to disability is disability-centred; it addresses the loss of opportunity for an individual to participate in mainstream society, albeit at a reduced level, in education and employment. There is a separation here between what is "physical" and "mental", so there should be no a priori other categories. It should be noted that the disability has an origin outside the person (age, illness or accident) and that it sets in gradually or permanently.
The WHO/World Bank Joint World Disability Report 2011 indicates, based on 2010 population estimates, that there are 1 billion people with disabilities in the world, or 15% of the world's population; in 1970 the estimate was 10%. The number is increasing as a result of ageing populations and also because of the increase in the number of chronic disabling diseases (diabetes, cardiovascular disease, mental illness). The public strategies envisaged include the development of fair procedures for assessing disability, clear eligibility criteria, regulation of service provision, creation of standards and concern for their enforcement, and funding of services for disabled people without financial means. Also noted is the exclusion of many persons with disabilities from decision-making concerning them, including the lack of choice or control over home assistance.

---

[8] http://www.un.org/disabilities/documents/convention/convoptprot-f.pdf
[9] https://www.unicef.fr/sites/default/files/userfiles/rapport_mondial_handicap_oms_2012.pdf

1.2.2 The European institutions and disability

In this section, we will now go down to the European level to see how disability is dealt with at the European level. We will proceed as we have done over the decades.

Article 15 of the 1961 *European Social Charter* affirms the right of persons with disabilities to education and employment.

The European Assembly in Strasbourg adopts the *European Charter for People with Disabilities in* 1981. The 1989 *European Social Charter of* the Council of Europe, in its Article 15, commits member states to take the necessary measures to ensure that persons with disabilities can exercise the right to independence, social integration and participation in the life of the community.

In 1992 the Council of Europe published a *Recommendation on a coherent policy for people with disabilities*. The European Union (EU) adopts the 1993 UN *Standard Rules on the Equalisation of Opportunities for Persons with Disabilities in* 1996, with a change of meaning since these will be the rules for "equal opportunities" and not for equalisation. The change of signifier loses some weight to the name: *equalization* indicates a dynamic to make equal, while *equality* is the goal to be achieved, which could be just a wish. In 1997, the EU signed the *Treaty of Amsterdam* which, in Article 13, prohibits all forms of discrimination on the grounds of "gender, race, age, disability, sexual orientation, religion or belief". This article expressly confers - and for the first time - on the Union the power to act in the field of disability. It thus recognises the problem of discrimination on the grounds of disability. Such discrimination is a criminal offence. Discrimination is to be understood as treating someone differently from what another person in a similar situation is, has been or would be treated.

The 2003 European Disability Forum (EDF)[10] proposes the following succinct definition of disability:

> *"Disability results from the interaction between the impairment, the resulting disability and the physical, social and cultural environment. This situation of disability results in partial or total loss of autonomy and/or difficulties in full participation. »*

We note the emergence of the term "disability status", which seems to indicate the importance of the environment in the development of social disadvantage. In 2000, the *Charter of Fundamental Rights of the* European Union was proclaimed in Nice; it was officially adopted by the Presidents of the European Commission, the European Parliament and the Council of the EU in 2007: it acquired binding legal force with the Treaty of Lisbon. In this Charter -

---

[10] http://www.edf-feph.org/default-fr.asp

applicable since 2009 - the rights are classified in six chapters: Dignity, Freedom, Equality, Solidarity, Citizenship, and Justice. Article 26 concerns persons with disabilities, who are recognised as having the right to benefit from measures to ensure their "independence", "social and professional integration" and "participation in community life". We will see that the idea of full participation in civic life will gain momentum in France in the following years. In 2003, the Council of Europe published the recommendation *Towards the full social integration of people with disabilities*. It implements the 2006-2015 Action Plan *for the promotion of the rights and full participation of people with disabilities in society: improving the quality of life of people with disabilities in Europe*. In 2010, the Council publishes the recommendation on *deinstitutionalisation of children with disabilities and their life in the community*.

1.2.3 20th century France and disability

In this section, we will look at how disability is taken into account in France. We keep the presentation by decades.

Since 1945, with the creation of the Social Security system, France has been creating institutions for "vulnerable persons",[11]thus taking care of - among other things - the disabled (Doat, 2010). The vulnerability of certain people is a theme that will also resurface in the 2000s, as we shall see below. We can note that the first French texts that take into account people with disabilities appeared in the 1940s, in Europe in the 1960s, and for the European authorities in the 1970s. Let us recall that it is our plan that led us not to have a chronological approach.

The law of 23 November 1957 is the first French law on disability; it only concerns adults (Vaginay, 2006). In this text, the term "disabled worker" appears; it also contains a definition of the "status" of a disabled worker attributed to

> *"...any person whose opportunities for acquiring and maintaining employment are effectively reduced by reason of an insufficiency or a decrease in his or her physical or mental capacity. »*

There is also a definition of "sheltered work". This law creates a higher council for the professional and social reclassification of disabled workers and establishes for them a theoretical quota of 10% priority employment in companies.

FROM THE 1960s onwards, efforts to conceptualize disability were developed in France, notably with psychiatrist Robert Lafon and occupational psychiatrist and physician Claude Veil. A disabled person must be considered as a person, his disability is only one element among many others; it is also a subject. Disability relates both to a certain situation and to the

---

[11] http://www-tmp.univ-brest.fr/digitalAssets/6/6052_Plaquette_Responsabilites_Vulnerabilite.pdf

awareness of it. (Veil, 1968). As far as children are concerned, the Improvement Classes for the Mentally Retarded were created in 1964; they are intended to receive children with intellectual deficits. A 1967 circular creates the Special Education Sections (SES), within the framework of the Secondary Education Colleges (CES), for the reception of young people with mild intellectual deficiencies. We may be surprised at the late appearance of these first legislative provisions; indeed, the education of disabled children developed in France in the 19th century, first for children with sensory deficiencies, then for so-called idiot children in psychiatric institutions. (Fèvre, 2011)

In the late 1970s, a report to the Prime Minister entitled *Study of the Problem of Disability Inadequacy of Persons with Disabilities* provided a definition of "disabled":

> *"Children, adolescents, and adults who, for various reasons, more or less serious, experience greater or lesser difficulties in being and acting like others, are maladjusted to the society of which they are a part.*
> *Of these, it is said that they are disabled by what they are experiencing, as a result of their physical, mental, character or social condition, disorders that constitute for them handicaps, i.e. weaknesses, particular servitudes in relation to normal. Normal [is] defined as the average of the abilities and chances of most individuals living in the same society."* (Bloch-Lainé, 1967).

It is a question of differentiating between disability and maladjustment: *disability is* confused with impairment, and *maladjustment* refers to the social effect of the disability. (Boucherat-Hue and Peretti, 2012). This approach focuses on the particularities of individuals compared to the average group. It introduces a reference to the norm, situating disability as the problem of deviation from the norm. It makes disability a difference, but to be understood as a difference to be reduced. In the definition of this report, we find the elements of the future International Classification of Impairments, elements that will prepare the 1975 policy text, and even the framework of environmental obstacles that some people place at the origin of disability situations. In 1974, the sociologist René Lenoir (1927-2017), in his book *Les Exclus,* approached disability from a particular angle:

> *"A person is disabled if, by reason of physical or mental disability, psychological behaviour or lack of training, he or she is unable to provide for himself or herself or requires constant care, or is segregated either by his or her own actions or those of the community" (*Lenoir, 1974*).*

Disability, seen as segregation, appears to him as a result of the disabled person himself, but also as coming from the environment in which he lives. The Labour Code was amended in 1974 for certain categories of persons temporarily without resources and without housing; it uses the term "socially handicapped" to designate them. The term is still used today, although it is criticized by some specialists in the social and medico-social sector. Two laws dated 30

June 1975 mark the disability sector: the law *on social and medico-social institutions,* which regulates the conditions for the creation, financing, training and status of staff in the sector's establishments and services; the law on *guidance for disabled persons,* which establishes the legal framework for action by the public authorities: prevention and detection of disabilities, compulsory education for disabled young people, access for disabled persons to all institutions and maintenance in the ordinary living environment whenever possible. The *Disabled Persons* Act enshrines the "integration" of persons with disabilities. With regard to children, it advocates "special education", which introduces the idea of "a different child, different treatment". During the discussions before the law was voted in the National Assembly, Simone Veil (1927-2017), Minister of Health, declared in April 1975: *"From now on, any person recognized as disabled by the departmental commissions will be considered as disabled", which* is a purely administrative definition of disability. However, it is thanks to this law that the generic concept of disability became established (Weber, 2011).

In 1987, the Law *for the Obligation of Employment of Disabled Workers, War Disabled and Similar* Persons introduced a legal employment rate of 6% of disabled persons for companies with more than 20 employees (known as the *Obligation of Employment of Disabled Workers* - OETH). It also creates the National Association for the Management of the Fund for the Professional Integration of Disabled Persons (AGEFIPH), which manages the allowances paid by companies that do not reach the 6% threshold. In 1988 the National Technical Centre for Research and Studies on Disability and Inadaptation (C.T.N.E.R.H.I.) and the National Institute of Health and Medical Research (INSERM) appropriated the text of the International Classification of Disabilities under the name *"International Classification of* Disabilities*: Impairments, Disabilities, Disadvantages (ICIDH)*". The term "disability" is then used as a generic word and no longer as a consequence of the encounter between a subject and his or her social environment. In this text, *disability* has a lesional bodily aspect: it is a loss of substance or an alteration of an anatomical, physiological or psychological structure or function. *Disability has a* functional aspect: resulting from an impairment, it refers to any partial or total reduction in the ability to perform an activity. *Disadvantage* has a situational aspect concerning social participation: it is a limitation or prohibition of the fulfilment of a normal social role taking into account age, gender, social and cultural factors; it results from the interaction between the person and the environment. Note that the medical diagnosis is of little importance; it is of interest only for the prognosis. ICH is person-centred and does not take into account the person's environment.

In the 1990s, organizations of persons with disabilities took up the philosophical-legal terms of the international human rights movements to initiate an international movement for the rights of persons with disabilities. In France, two laws of the 1990s concerned disability: in 1990 "on the protection of persons against discrimination on the grounds of their state of health or disability", and in 1991 the law "designed to promote the accessibility to disabled persons of residential premises, workplaces and facilities open to the public". With regard to children and adolescents, a circular of 1995 established Integration Pedagogical Units (UPIs) in some colleges, designed to bring together adolescents "with mental disabilities". Another circular of 1996 created Sections of Adapted General and Vocational Education (SEGPA) in some collèges, for "pupils with serious and persistent educational difficulties" who are encountering difficulties and disruptions in terms of efficiency.

> *It is not "without mental retardation [which] does not translate into disability and disadvantage [according to WHO criteria]. ...] The SEGPAs do not have to take in students solely because of behavioural problems or difficulties directly related to the understanding of the French language.* »

A circular of 2002 sets out the various school integration schemes, recalling that "each school, each collège, each lycée has a vocation to welcome, without discrimination, children and adolescents with disabilities or illnesses whose families request integration at school". If "major difficulties objectively make such integration impossible", alternative solutions are proposed: school integration classes (CLIS) in elementary school, and UPIs, which are kept for secondary school.

We thus see a parallel evolution between the legislative provisions for adults and for children or adolescents, in the disjointed fields of disability and national education; a rapprochement from a legal point of view will only take place in 2005.

1.2.4 French legislation at the beginning of the 21st century

In this section, we will look in more detail at the laws of the 2000s, in particular those of January 2002 on social and medico-social action and those of February 2005 on disability, which have shaken up representations and practices in the field of disability.

The 2002 law on the *renewal of social and* medico-social *action* reforms the 1975 law on social and medico-social institutions. It affirms the rights of persons accommodated in institutions and accompanied in social and medico-social institutions and services (ESSMS), and living and reception facilities (LVA). First of all, it lists the *eight rights* recognised to each person: respect for their dignity, integrity, privacy, intimacy and security; free choice between adapted services; quality individualised support; confidentiality of information concerning them; access to all documents concerning them; information on their fundamental rights; participation in the implementation of their project; the right not to be separated from their family. It then deals with the *seven tools* needed to make them a reality: the Charter of Rights and Freedoms; the welcome booklet; the operating regulations; the residence contract and the individual accompanying document; the settlement or service project; advice on social life and other forms of user participation; qualified persons. This 2002 law also introduces, alongside the departmental social and medico-social organisation schemes that appeared at the time of the decentralisation laws of 1983 and 1986, regional and national schemes. The purpose of the plans, which must be drawn up in accordance with the health organization plans, is to: assess the needs of the population; take stock of the social and medico-social supply; determine the prospects and objectives for the development of the supply; specify the framework for cooperation and coordination between institutions and services; and define the criteria for evaluating the actions implemented. The law also establishes the obligation for social and medico-social establishments and services to carry out regular internal and external evaluations, failing which they may lose their approval.

The *Social Modernization Act of* 2002 concerns the right to work, health and housing. Title I "Health, Solidarity, Social Security" contains Chapter III, which concerns pensioners, the elderly and the disabled. Article 53 establishes as a "national obligation" the prevention and detection of disability, the recognition of access by all disabled persons to the fundamental rights recognized to all citizens, the guarantee of a minimum level of resources, and access to all areas of work, culture and leisure. The disabled person has the right to compensation for his or her disability. The Act establishes the Departmental Advisory Councils for Persons with Disabilities (CDCPH). Here we find a transposition of *the* provisions of the *Charter of Fundamental Rights of the* European Union of 2000 concerning the participation of people with disabilities in community life. I have noted that within the CDCPH, disabled people themselves are under-represented: sometimes physically disabled people sit on the CDCPH, rarely blind or deaf people, never people with intellectual or mental disabilities.

The *Charter of Human Rights and Freedoms welcomed is based* on the 1996 order reforming public and private hospitalization concerning the *Hospitalized Patient Charter and* is set by an interministerial order of 2003. It comprises twelve articles: the principle of non-discrimination; the right to appropriate support; the right to information; the principle of free choice, informed consent and participation of the person; the right to renunciation; the right to respect for family ties; the right to protection; the right to autonomy; the principle of prevention and support; the right to exercise civil rights; the right to religious practice; and respect for the dignity of the person and his or her privacy.

The 2004 *Act on Solidarity for the Independence of the Elderly and Disabled Persons* established the National Solidarity Fund for Autonomy (CNSA), which is responsible for helping to finance actions to promote the autonomy of disabled persons and dependent elderly persons. The "solidarity day" (initially Whit Monday), worked by each employee, is unpaid, but the equivalent of the salary is paid by employers to the CNSA; this fund finances the personalized compensation benefit for disabled persons, as well as part of the cost of the

APA[12]. This is a clear rapprochement between the provisions concerning disabled persons and the elderly, which historically constitutes what is known as the "medico-social sector", although since 1975 all texts have referred only to the much broader "social and medico-social" sector (CASF, art. L 312-1, art. L 116-1).

In 2005, the *Law for Equal Rights and Opportunities, Participation and Citizenship of Persons with Disabilities* gave France its definition of *disability:*

> *"Any limitation of activity or restriction of participation in social life suffered by a person in his or her environment as a result of a substantial, lasting or permanent impairment of one or more physical, sensory, mental, cognitive or psychological functions, a multiple disability or a disabling health condition constitutes a disability. »*

This law brings fundamental changes to meet the expectations of disabled people: the right to disability compensation, to schooling, to employment, to accessibility. With regard to children, it establishes the principle that all children should be accommodated in the school closest to their home, and for disabled pupils, a Personalized Schooling Plan (PPS) has been set up. We can see here that this Act brings the provisions concerning children with disabilities and schools closer together. Act 2005-102 establishes the right to compensation for the consequences of a disability. This right to compensation is broadly conceived; it complements ordinary law (principle of subsidiarity). The disabled person has access to the ordinary law of the population in loss of autonomy; then, when necessary, to the adaptation of the ordinary law; and finally, when specific needs are not met, to the development of appropriate special measures. This law reinforces the CNSA's missions: as a public institution, it provides technical support to the departmental, regional and national networks; it is also a fund that distributes the financial resources it receives (22.6 billion euros in the initial budget for 2015). It is responsible for participating in the financing of assistance for the autonomy of disabled persons and dependent elderly persons. It is supposed to guarantee equal treatment throughout the national territory for all persons with disabilities by distributing resources fairly. It is responsible for providing expertise, information and leadership on the quality of the services provided. It is responsible for research and encouraging innovation.

The 2005 French law on disability does not include the concept of interaction between the person and his or her environment. Stiker (2009) wonders whether disability is merely an administrative category defining a fragile population by arbitrary limits. It could simply be a representation, i.e. a shared social image. He elaborates that perhaps disability does not exist,

---

[12] Personalized autonomy allowance

that it is always about people with their singularity and their personal psychic repercussions. The concept of *disability status, which* appeared in 2002, is not included in this 2005 law.

1.2.5 The CDM

In this last section of this chapter, we will discover and comment on a provision of Law 2005-102: the Departmental House for Disabled Persons (MDPH) and its two operating bodies (the multidisciplinary team and the CDAPH[13]), and then its tools for assessing disability and appeals against its decisions.

The Disability Act sets up, in each French department, a MDPH, a one-stop shop that provides reception, information, advice and support for people with disabilities and their families. It is responsible for informing the population about disability issues, receiving and listening to disabled persons, assessing situations of disability and drawing up the compensation plan, taking decisions on the granting of benefits or referral to establishments and services, monitoring compensation, support and mediation. The MDPH is administered by an Executive Commission (COMEX) chaired by the President of the Departmental Council. Its members, appointed for four years, are drawn half from the Department, one quarter from the State and social protection bodies, and one quarter from associations representing disabled persons or their families. Within the MDPH, the multidisciplinary team (EP) is made up of doctors, occupational therapists, psychologists, specialists in social work and schooling. Based on the person's life project, the EP assesses the person's disability situation, determines the rate of incapacity, checks the eligibility criteria for benefits and assesses the need for compensation. The EP is, most of the time, generalist: it deals with all disabilities; it is mainly composed of generalist training professionals who are supposed to have a competence for each of the disabilities. Thus, I have been able to observe that a lack of specialization concerning *psychological disability* can lead to dramatic decisions being taken for certain particularly fragile people, due to a lack of knowledge of the particularities of this disability.
Also at the MDPH, the Disability Independence Rights Commission is responsible for making decisions regarding the rights of persons with disabilities, based on the assessment and proposals of the EP. In particular, it is responsible for the Recognition of the status of disabled worker (RQTH), awarding compensation benefits, notifying referrals to social and medico-social institutions or services. The Disability Compensation Benefit (PCH) must enable the person with a disability to achieve greater autonomy in the areas of mobility, personal maintenance, communication and relations with others. The idea is to enable the person to have access to the whole life of a citizen, as a person of the same age and social conditions as

---

[13] Commission on the Rights and Independence of Persons with Disabilities

him or her and who is not disabled. The disabled person is notified of the date on which his or her file will be examined; he or she may attend the session and be assisted by a person of his or her choice. The decision that is taken is notified to the person in writing by the President of the CDAPH: it is valid for one to five years. Failure to respond to his or her request within four months of the submission of his or her file is deemed to be a rejection decision.

The CDAPH is made up of twenty-three members: four representatives of the department (departmental councillor, director of autonomy, technical expert, etc.), four from the State (DDCS,[14]DIRECCTE,[15]Academic Directorate, ARS, etc.[16]), two from the health insurance and family benefits organisations (CAF,[17]CPAM, MSA,[18]RSI,[19]etc.) and two from the private sector (CAF, CPAM,[20]MSA, RSI, etc.).), two of the trade unions (employers and/or employees), one representative of the parents' associations, seven of the associations of disabled persons and their families (among those recognized as representative in the department), one member of the CDCPH, two of the organizations managing establishments for disabled persons. The number of alternates is not limited. What I have been able to observe is that within the CDAPH most of the administrators are not specialists in disability (representatives of the state, social agencies and trade unions) and that few are representatives of the disabled themselves (it is often parents who sit on the board), so that the expertise of the CDAPH rests on the representatives of the families of the disabled and perhaps also on a few professionals from associations managing establishments for people with disabilities. Thus, this commission, which takes decisions that are extremely important for people with disabilities, can - in good faith - because of its lack of knowledge, for example, of a disability (particularly a psychological one), take decisions that run counter to the needs of certain particularly vulnerable people. Of course, the MDPHs provide training for the people who sit on the CDAPH. However, these trainings, at the rate of one or two days per year, if they allow to get to know the functioning of the institution, only give a very fragmented vision of each of the disabilities: it is not in half a day that one can understand, for example, what a psychological disability is. I have also noted that many CDAPHs have split into two commissions, one for children and adolescents, and another for adults, reproducing the previous functioning of the CCPE[21], CCSD[22] and COTOREP[23]; some decisions are thus difficult to take for young adults in particular, given the different age limits according to the institutions (15, 16, 18, 20, 21, 25, 30). Other CDAPHs have specialized by category of disability. Some have set up restricted commissions to speed up the procedure for situations

[14] Departmental Directorate of Social Cohesion
[15] Regional Directorate for Enterprise, Competition, Consumer Affairs, Labour and Employment
[16] Regional Health Agency
[17] Family allowance fund
[18] Agricultural Social Mutual
[19] Social regime for the self-employed
[20] Primary Health Insurance Fund
[21] Preschool and Elementary Advisory Committee
[22] Second Degree Consultative Commission
[23] Technical Commission for Vocational Guidance and Reclassification

which apparently did not seem to pose any difficulty in reaching a decision; I have seen, in some of these commissions, either the request for a referral to the plenary committee by one of the members of the restricted committee for a more in-depth study of a case whose difficulty had obviously escaped the EP, or, in the case of a drawing of lots in the plenary committee of cases passed by the restricted committee, the complete resumption of the study of cases whose complexity had been underestimated by the EP, in particular in the case of mental disability.
The CDM is designed as a one-stop shop for all people with disabilities. Whereas previously the entry into the mechanism was different for children (CCPE), adolescents (CCSD) grouped within the CDES, and adults (COTOREP), the MDPH is supposed to welcome all persons regardless of their age; in fact, many MDPHs have kept the previous functioning, by creating specialized youth and adult commissions. The main criticism of this new system concerns the fate of children: until 2005, when teaching teams identified children with learning difficulties, parents were received in CCPE centres, run by both National Education and DDASS staff[24]; parents could be informed of their child's difficulties and the solutions that could be put in place, including referral to a medical and social care system. Today, parents are asked to go to the one-stop shop to request a study of their child's file, but this shop is called Maison pour les Handicapés (House for the Disabled), and many parents are not prepared to agree that their child is disabled! Their representation of disability does not allow them to attribute this term to their child. Thus, many parents cannot take the first step to find the best solution for their child. Some departments have seized the opportunity afforded by the law to bring together within the same body the arrangements for disabled and elderly persons by creating Departmental Autonomy Houses (Maisons départementales de l'autonomie (MDA)); perhaps with this more neutral name, some parents will be less reluctant to go through the door of this one-stop shop.

Tools to measure disability

The *Guide-Barrier is the*[25] result of a decree of 1993; it establishes eight major categories of disabilities: intellectual disabilities and behavioural difficulties, psychological disabilities, hearing disabilities, language and speech disabilities, vision disabilities, visceral and general disabilities, musculoskeletal disabilities and aesthetic disabilities. This guide is based on the ICH. In 2007, an update adds the following: visceral and general impairments (impairments in cardiorespiratory, digestive, hepatic, renal and urinary functions, endocrine, metabolic and enzyme functions, immunohematological functions). *Psychiatric deficiencies* include disorders of volition, thought, perception, communication, behaviour, mood, consciousness and alertness, intellectual, emotional and affective disorders and the somatic expression of psychiatric disorders. The *psychic deficiencies of the adult* are developed :

---

[24] Departmental Directorate of Social Affairs
[25] https://www.legifrance.gouv.fr/affichTexte.do?cidTexte=JORFTEXT000000517921ategorieLien=id

- *Volition disorders* include apragmatism, negativism, obsessive compulsions, ambivalence and inhibition.
- *Thought disorders* (course and content) include obsessive thinking, flight or inconsistency of ideas, slowness of thought, drivel, impoverishment of thought and delirium.
- *Perceptual disorders* include illusions, hallucinations and derealizations.
- *Communication disorders* are at the level of language, but exclude aphasia treated separately; they include disorders of form, content of language and gestural expression: logorrhoea, preciousness, donkey cock, neologisms, echolalia, discordance, parasitism, mimicry, gestural or deficient stereotypes, functional disorders (stuttering, mutism) and autistic withdrawal.
- *Behavioural disorders* include aggression, agitation, acting out, self-injury, phobic behaviour, obsessive rituals, instability and shyness.
- *Mood disorders* are depressive or hypomanic disorders, manic-depressive psychosis, states of excitement or depression, manic state, psychomotor agitation, flight of ideas, severe insomnia, melancholic state (abulia, moral pain, self-blame, psychomotor retardation).
- *Disorders of consciousness and alertness* are not detailed; they relate, in the facts observed by us, to the notion of endangerment.
- *Intellectual disorders* include disorders following an early mental illness (coarse personality, possibly illiteracy), mental retardation as measured by the Intellectual Quotient (IQ), and late-onset disorders, i.e., disorders of the emotional and affective life including anxiety, anguish, doubt, emotional indifference, emotional discord, emotional instability, character disorders, emotional immaturity, and shyness.
- *The somatic expression of psychiatric disorders* consists of a somatisation with a type of subjective complaints that disrupt daily and professional life and can even lead to serious and disabling alterations in the general state of health.

Basic or essential Ac*ts of Daily Living* (ADLs) include the following activities:

- behave in a logical and sensible way,
- find their way through time and place,
- ensure personal hygiene,
- dressing and undressing appropriately,
- eating prepared foods,

- assume the hygiene of urinary and faecal elimination,
- carry out movements (getting up, sitting down, lying down) and displacements.

We will come back to this *scale guide* later, since it is this tool that is always used to qualify the disability - and therefore the psychological disability - and to measure its seriousness, its consequences for the person and the help to be provided.

Law 2002-2 had instituted the AGGIR (Autonomie gérontologie groupes iso-ressources) grid[26] as a tool for issuing the Allocation personnalisée à l'autonomie for the elderly. A team composed of paramedical (nurse) and social (social service assistant) personnel assesses the person's difficulties at home. Composed of a simple questionnaire, the grid is based on the person's answers to measure his or her difficulties in carrying out certain daily living activities: getting up, eating, washing, etc. The grid is then used to determine the person's level of difficulty. A software program transforms the answers into a number, from 1 to 6, from the heaviest dependency to the absence of any difficulty. Françoise Weber (2011) regrets that the same grid is not used for both the elderly and the disabled, the one used for disability being more complicated and more like a biographical questionnaire. This idea of a common approach to the two situations will be found later in the notion of "loss of autonomy".

While the Scale Guide is used by the multidisciplinary CDM team to determine the disability rate of the adult person with a disability, a *Multidimensional Assessment Guide* (GÉVA) enables it to carry out the assessment of any disability; for children and adolescents in school, it is declined in 2015 in a GÉVA-Sco.
GEVA is used for the allocation of the Disability Compensation Benefit (DCB). It is very different from the scale guide since its purpose is not to define a rate of disability but the degree of autonomy of the disabled person. With this tool, the aim is to make a multidimensional, multidisciplinary and partnership-based assessment covering all the dimensions of the person's life.
This guide consists of eight sections:

- *the family and social environment*: resources, administrative situation ;
- *the physical environment*: housing, neighbourhood, means of transport ;
- *education, training, work*;
- *the medical aspect*: psychological deficiencies, treatment, care (consultations, hospitalizations, nurse, psychologist);
- *the psychological aspect*: tests, psycho-clinical analysis of the situation;

---

[26] https://www.service-public.fr/particuliers/vosdroits/F1229

- *activities*: mobility, personal maintenance, domestic life, daily life, relationships with others, learning, knowledge application (focusing attention, memorizing, decision-making);
- *the assistance provided*: intervention by the family and friends, health care, care by a service (SAVS,[27]SAMSAH[28], household help, etc.);
- *preparation of the compensation plan*: human assistance needs falling within the scope of the compensation benefit, human assistance needs not falling within the scope of the compensation benefit, allocation of human assistance time and all other needs.

After the assessment of the person's needs by the multidisciplinary team, the allocation of the compensation benefit is decided by the CDAPH. Component 6 of the AVSM measures activities and functional abilities:

- activities in the field of "mobility, manipulation" (getting around),
- the domain "general tasks and requirements, relations with others" (orienting oneself in time, space, having relations in accordance with social rules),
- communication" (conducting a conversation, using communication devices and techniques),
- in the area of knowledge translation, learning (acquiring know-how, application of know-how).

It points out that the constraints linked to treatment can aggravate impairments and limit activities, and that account should be taken of people's potential and adaptive skills, of the evolution of disorders (prospects for improvement or aggravation), and of the fluctuating nature of certain impairments or disabilities. One of the problems in using this evaluation guide is that it is based on the statements of the person with a disability; thus, a person who is unaware of his difficulties, or who is in denial of his disabilities, is unable to give his interlocutor the reliable information he would need to make his evaluation; this is particularly visible in the case of psychological disability.

The disabled adult can apply to the HRDM for a minimum income, which in law is called the Disabled Adult Allowance (DAA).

- The AAH is automatically awarded to any person with a permanent disability rate of at least 80%.

---

[27] Social support service

[28] Medical-social support service for disabled adults

- It is also awarded to any person whose rate of permanent disability is at least 50% and less than 80% and for whom the CDAPH recognizes, in view of his or her disability, a Substantial and Permanent Restriction on Access to Employment (SSDAE). To make its decision, the CDAPH relies on the assessment carried out by the CDM Multidisciplinary Team, on the basis of the references defined by the Code of Social Action and Families (CASF), in particular the GÉVA. This evaluation includes an analysis of the consequences of impairments, activity limitations and other effects of the disability, as well as the possibilities for professional integration.

To be eligible for AAH, the disability must be expected to last at least one year, but stabilization of the medical situation is not necessary. The progressive nature of the disorder, the fluctuating nature of certain impairments or disabilities, must be taken into account in determining the AAH. The elements of assessment for the GEDI are both personal and external factors; among the personal factors, it is the impact of the impairments that must be measured, but also the possible effects of treatment. However, the PE can carry out an assessment at a given time, whereas certain pathologies are particularly fluctuating; this is the case, for example, for *mental disability*. On the other hand, a large part of the evaluation is based on a dialogue with the disabled person, who in some cases, especially in the case of mental disability, is not aware of his or her difficulties. Some MDPHs involve relatives by submitting a questionnaire to them.

Appeals against decisions of the CDAPH

Decisions taken by the CDAPH are subject to an ex gratia appeal to the CDM. Appeals are not frequent; in the event of an appeal, the CDAPH does not often go back on its initial decision, except, as I have observed, when people come to meet the Commission and explain the particularity of their case, which had escaped the members. However, some people suffering from a very disabling disability will not be able to face the Commission, even in a restricted configuration, even accompanied, as in some cases of mental disability, for example. I was a member of the CDAPH in Sarthe for three years.

Until 2018, decisions of the CDAPH could be appealed to the Disability Tribunal (DTC). The TCI was created in 1994, imposed on France by the European Union. There was one TCI per region; this judicial mechanism disappeared in 2019. It was composed of an honorary magistrate, two assessors (employers' and employees' organisations) and an expert doctor, present at the hearing with voting rights - a general practitioner, but who could request the opinion of a doctor who had two months to make his report. A case could be brought before the CFI even if an appeal had not been made. A first stage known as conciliation made it possible to summon the parties (the complainant and the MDPH, for example) to try to find an arrangement. The MDPH rarely appeared at this hearing. In the second stage, judgment was pronounced on certain decisions of the CDAPH (disability rate and RSDAE in particular). In fact, decisions were often made on the same day, at the end of the hearings. Decisions concerning the RQTH and parking cards are the responsibility of the Administrative Tribunal (AT). The TCI also judged appeals against certain social security decisions (incapacity, work accidents, disability). The judgment of the TCI had certain peculiarities; for example, it applied the adversarial principle : The applicant had to be present at the hearing, he often came with a file; the MDPH was convened at the hearing; it was an oral procedure; during the appeal, the application could change and any other requests could be made; one could be accompanied by any person of one's choice, a lawyer was not necessary; the hearing was public; the procedure was free of charge; travel expenses were covered by the court; the application was processed on the basis of documents only; the CFI doctor examined the person on the spot and immediately transmitted his conclusions at the hearing in the presence of the applicant; if necessary, the doctor could travel to the home. I sat as an assessor judge for three years at the T.C.I. of Sarthe.

The judgment of the CFI was subject to appeal to the National Court of Disability and Tariffing of Insurance and Industrial Accidents (CNITATT), which was sitting in Amiens. The judgment and the appeal could be overturned by the Social Chamber of the Court of Cassation. We can note that appeals to the TCI were relatively rare[29], but that in many cases, people obtained satisfaction in opposition to the decisions of the CDAPH. Thus, for example, concerning mental disability, I could see that one of the criteria retained by a CDAPH for the refusal of an AAH, namely the absence of medical follow-up, was immediately contested by the TCI and that the allowance was granted to the person concerned only on the basis of the assessment - by the doctor - of his incapacity to work. However, we should note that the TCI was composed of a retired magistrate (or lawyer) and two representatives of trade unions who were not required to have any expertise in the field of disability, even if, during their three-year term of office, they were learning their trade; this is why, most of the time, the magistrates relied on the opinion of the doctor who, himself, concerning certain disabilities - such as mental disability -, could sometimes rely on the expertise of a specialist colleague - a doctor who was a sapiteur - to propose a decision to the court. Thus, a medical opinion was often at the origin of a judgment of the ICJ. I noticed that some judges practically only addressed themselves to the doctor, to the great disappointment of disabled persons and/or their relatives; indeed, as the case was judged in twenty to thirty minutes - including the medical consultation - no time should be wasted. Moreover, sometimes one to two years had elapsed between the data subject's appeal and the hearing. Even if the judgement was delivered at the end of the session, it was still necessary to wait at least one month before receiving it by post. I was also

[29] The December 2017 CNSA report indicates an ex gratia or litigation rate of between 0.5 per cent and 4.5 per cent depending on the department.

able to note that in most cases the two assessors had not read the file before the session and did not consult it during the session; only the magistrate and the doctor seemed to know it.
While it was clearly stated at the bottom of the CDAPH notifications that decisions were subject to an ex gratia appeal to the HRDM and to challenge before the ICC, it should be noted that the time limit for appeal was two months; beyond that, it was time-barred. It was not uncommon for people with disabilities not to read the mail to the end and not to know that they could appeal; in the case of mental disability, it was not uncommon for the person considering an appeal to miss the two-month time limit for lodging an appeal. We will also see that, for some people in a situation of disability of psychological origin who do not have a well-insured notion of time and who have difficulties in initiating a procedure, recourse to the court seems impossible. Moreover, the idea of having to physically appear before a court to challenge the MDPH on its decision discouraged more than one disabled person.
Faced with the increase in the number of appeals before the court, a department in financial difficulty had decided that, in the event that the CIT granted a PCH in disagreement with the CDAPH, it would systematically challenge the decision before the CNITATT: thus, if this body did not follow the CIT in its decision, the department could make a saving; but otherwise, given the time limits (about two years), it would ensure its cash flow. We will see later that even a perfect knowledge of the workings of the HRDM and appeals is not sufficient for some people to decide, given their incapacity, to undertake an ex gratia appeal, let alone a legal action.
Medical confidentiality was not respected in this instance, particularly when it came to the question of mental disability, since the sessions were public and closed sessions were very rarely requested.

Since 2019, appeals against CDAPH decisions are made to the Tribunal de Grande Instance (TGI), but only after an appeal to the MDPH called Rapo (Mandatory Prior Administrative Appeal).[30]

1.3 Vulnerable people

In this third chapter, we will broaden our view of disability in the French context to see that it is also part of a broader concept of vulnerability.

The 2007 Act on the *Legal Protection of Adults* refocuses the efforts of the judiciary on adults made vulnerable by disability or old age.

---

[30] https://www.cnsa.fr/actualites-agenda/actualites/reforme-des-modalites-de-recours-contre-les-decisions-des-mdph-et-des-conseils-departementaux

"Persons of full age receive the protection of their person and property that their condition or situation requires.... This protection shall be established and ensured with respect for individual freedoms, fundamental rights and the dignity of the person. Its purpose is the interest of the protected person. It shall, as far as possible, promote the autonomy of the protected person. It is a duty of families and the public community. »

(Civil Code, art. 415)

The law is based on three principles: *necessity, subsidiarity* and *proportionality.* A protective measure is put in place only in the case of impairment of mental faculties (necessity); a protective measure of the curatorship or guardianship type is not put in place if a lighter measure may suffice, such as a MASP[31] (subsidiarity); the measure must be proportionate to the real difficulties of the person and personalised (proportionality). The measure is pronounced for a maximum of five years. The disabled person can choose his or her curator or guardian. The disabled person may not be represented in certain personal cases - recognition of a child, for example -. The guardian can only represent the person in cases expressly indicated in the judgment. For decisions seriously affecting the physical integrity of the person, the judge must be seized. In the case of guardianship, the judge shall indicate whether the person has the right to vote. The law also introduces the mandate for future protection: a person may designate in advance the person who will be able to represent him or her in the event of an impairment of his or her mental faculties.

This law is a major turning point for the recognition of the status of full citizen of the disabled person. It is surprising to see on the ground how it has gone unnoticed in many private organisations serving disabled people and even how it is ignored in some public institutions. Thus, in 2015, to a remark made to a director of MDPH that a file should not be studied in CDAPH on the grounds that the request did not come from the person himself but from his guardian, I was told that "the guardian represents the disabled person in all acts of civil life", which is no longer the case since this law of 2007.

The Chossy Report

In 2010, Deputy Chossy was entrusted by the Secretary of State for the Family and Solidarity with a parliamentary mission *aimed at changing mentalities and society's view of people with disabilities.* His report[32] calls on us to move from "disability as an attribute" to "disability as a situation", to conceive it in terms of a "constructed" context and not a "given" one. Disability thus appears in an environment that needs to be changed to remove barriers and for which facilitators need to be invented. The report calls for a shift from "taking care" to "taking into

---

31 Personalized social support measure, set up by the Department for persons receiving social minima and who request it.

32 http://www.assemblee-nationale.fr/12/rapports/r2038.asp

account", for the person not to be reduced to the role of "patient", to that of a burden, a burden, a heaviness; it advocates "support" in the sense of "walking alongside the person" and by promoting his or her autonomy as much as possible. It calls for marginality to be banished so that each person has a place in society as a whole, for a shift from the "destitution of speech" to the recognition of its "irreplaceable value": that the voices of disabled people be heard and that their expertise be recognized in decisions that concern them. The Chossy report deplores the use, in the 2005 law, of the term "persons with disabilities" and prefers "persons in a situation of disability":

> *"It is indeed a question of defining the state in which the person concerned finds himself, while specifying, as the law says (art. 2), that the person's environment is indeed a factor to be considered among others.*
> *One is in a situation of disability when the moment is fleeting, temporary, in front of one's environment.* "(Chossy, 2010, p.12).

We see in this report the importance of the environment in the disability situation, which we will find in other contexts.

The Chossy report concludes with recommendations concerning the vocabulary used: replace "handicap" by "capacity restriction", "accessibility" by "access to everything for all", "deficient" by "otherwise capable" (Quebec), "unable to invest in ordinary life" by "different but competent", "different person" by "singular person", "benevolent" by "tolerant", "beneficiary" by "contributor", "life project" by "life course", "taking charge" by "consideration, accompaniment", "placement" by "reception". Concerning the term "disability", the Chossy report is categorical:

> *"We must definitively banish the terms "disability", "handicapped", which are synonymous with indignity, or "situation of disability", which are stigmatizing, in order to refocus reflection not only on the person and his or her status as a disabled person, but on his or her capacity for active participation and involvement - even modest - in society.* "(Chossy, 2010, p.17).

It is worth noting a change in Chossy's text itself, since he says he prefers "person with a disability" to "person in a situation of disability", but further on he recommends banning this expression "situation of disability", which he still finds stigmatizing. For my part, I have not found any other term to replace "disability". Can I propose, from autonomous, "oligonome" (if not hyponome)?

We will now refocus our study on people with disabilities.

The Piveteau Report

In 2014, the report *Zero without solution: the collective duty to allow a seamless life course for people with disabilities and their families*, also known as the "Piveteau report",[33]named after its author, State Councillor Denis Piveteau, the first director of the CNSA, will be published. It reminds us of our society's duties towards the most severely disabled people, "a collective duty to enable a seamless life course for people with disabilities and their families". Zero without a solution means that every disabled person must be able to benefit from the support they need; it is a question of avoiding "breaks in the journey", particularly at critical stages of life (passage from childhood to adulthood, from the latter to old age; etc.) or absences from care or support, particularly in the case of serious behavioural problems. The central role of the CDMs is affirmed as "pivotal elements", "assemblers" and "companions". It is no longer a question of financing "places" but "quality territorial responses" (modular responses). In order to move from an obligation of means to an obligation of results, the main recommendations can be summarised as follows: personalised analysis of needs and prioritisation of responses; orientation of the system and setting up of a coordinator; setting up of an emergency medico-social system; administrative simplification and derogatory powers given to the MDPHs for certain complementary support measures. The report recommends replacing the "single" decision of the CDAPH by a policy decision "which states what is desirable" and a Global Support Plan (GSP) "which states what is possible, making it effectively enforceable".
Since 2013, several departments have decided to bring together the territorial actors concerned by elderly and disabled people, thus taking over the representation of a "medico-social" sector. For example, in Sarthe, the regional schemes (elderly people, disabled people, child-family and integration) were merged in 2015. Other departments - as we have seen - have chosen to create Departmental Houses of Autonomy (MDA) - not to be confused with Departmental Houses for Adolescents -. The attributions of the MDPHs are then included in those of the MDAs.
This development leads me to question the notion of *dependency*. From a medical point of view, the term addiction means

> "*...the condition of persons who cannot perform the essential acts of daily life without assistance: handicapped, chronically ill, infirm or demented elderly people.* "(Weber, 2011)

Dependency is one aspect of disability, as a severe hardship of daily life due to impairments.
In 2016, in 23 departments, a version of the *Zero without solution* advocated by Denis Piveteau will be implemented in the form of a roadmap called *Une réponse accompagnée pour tous*. It consists of preventing disabled people from being cut off from the mainstream and being left without a reception and care solution due to lack of space in a medical-social structure. The roadmap, which is intended to be innovative and not experimental, begins with a first wave that is divided into four areas. The first area, led by the CNSA, consists of a permanent referral

---

[33] http://social-sante.gouv.fr/IMG/pdf/Rapport_Zero_sans_solution_.pdf

system, where the MDPH is a "assembler" of local solutions for complex cases in order to offer tailor-made solutions; service platforms are set up to invent coordinated support solutions; transitional accommodation is created for disabled people who need to be distanced from their usual environment. Another focus of the roadmap, steered by the general secretariat of the inter-ministerial committee on disability, is devoted to peer support; the delegates of the rights defender are involved in this; the aim is to train people with disabilities so that they can intervene in the training of professionals. Under the guidance of the general secretariat of the ministries responsible for social affairs, it consists of building a "territorialized response", with the idea of a complementary partnership between the department and the national education system. The last axis is that of support for change, piloted by the General Directorate for Social Cohesion (DGCS), for "a simplification of administrative tasks with low added value".

In 2016, the government is also setting up *Pôles de compétences et de prestations externalisées (*PCPE) (*Centres of expertise and outsourced services)*: this involves creating mechanisms to finance the work of liberal professionals in the homes of disabled persons (psychologists, educators, etc.), as part of a Personalized Disability Compensation Plan (PPCH), the Personalized Schooling Plan and, where appropriate, the Global Support Plan. These direct interventions provide the necessary and coordinated services of professionals from different fields (health, medical and social), in accordance with the Recommendations for Good Practice (RBP) of the High Authority for Health (HAS) and the National Agency for Social and Medical-Social Assessment (ANESM).

1.4 The process of producing disability

To conclude this first part on disability, in this fourth chapter, we will discuss a concept that seems not to have been really taken into account in the French context[34], that of the "Processus de production du handicap" (PPH) in Quebec, which takes into account the person's environment when assessing disability.
François Tosquelles wrote in 1964:

> *"If the profoundly retarded, like everyone else, has the vocation to become a subject, it is nevertheless true that he, more than anyone else, finds himself subject both to the conditioning of what might be called the accidents of his corporeality, and to the conditioning of the inter-social environment. This environment whose dependence he is led to accept, even at the price of the abrasion of all his desires.* »

---

[34] However, some occupational therapists use it

The fact that we can take into account the specific difficulties of the disabled person, but also of his or her environment, will not be theorized until much later in Quebec.

Philipp Wood is a British doctor, rheumatologist and epidemiologist. He was Professor of Public Health at the University of Manchester. The WHO, which wants to define the health status of people with chronic diseases, calls on Wood and a group of international experts. Based on the proposals of André Grossiord, a doctor at the Raymond Poincaré Hospital in Garches - who distinguishes between impairments and their consequences - the work is leading to a new vision of disability: whatever their causes (illness), *disabilities* result from organic or anatomical *deficits*, which lead to *incapacities in* carrying out acts of daily social life, which can lead to social *disadvantages, in* particular by making *participation in* certain social roles inaccessible. This proposal was accepted by the WHO in 1980 and became known as the *International classification of impairments, disabilities and handicaps (*see above).

In fact, from 1977 onwards, works entitled *Processes of production of disability were published,* which brought to light, as the context of a situation of disability, the "habits of life" of people, that is to say, all personal and cultural arrangements.

Patrick Fougeyrollas is a Quebec anthropologist; in the 1980s, the Office des personnes handicapées du Québec (OPHQ) recruited him to help create a program for the integration of people with disabilities (Hamonet, 2010). Shortly after the publication of Wood's classification, this program was disseminated in a report entitled *À part égale*. In this report, the issue of disability is dealt with from the perspective of different human activities, based in particular on the person's "lifestyle habits" and environment.

In 1986, Fougeyrollas and his working group, proposed a model they called "Disability Production Process" (DPP). Among the environmental factors, he distinguishes between those that are personal and those that are contextual. The group believes that the reference to "disability" is awkward because "it stigmatizes by evoking infirmity". A definition of disability was proposed:

> *"Disability is a disruption in a person's ability to carry out lifestyle choices based on age, gender, socio-cultural identity, resulting from impairments or disabilities on the one hand, and barriers resulting from environmental factors on the other. »*

Fougeyrollas and his team, within the Canadian and Quebec societies of the International Classification of Disabilities (ICDH), will develop the classification of disabilities of the World Health Organization and in particular will introduce environmental factors within the International Classification of Functionality.

The concept of the *Disability Production Process was* born out of a movement of demands by people suffering from marginalization due to physical or mental differences. In an attempt to explain the causes of the "marginalization of bodies and minds", the DPP refers to three fundamental concepts: impairment, functional limitation and disability. *Impairment* is objectifiable; it results from a biological singularity, an abnormality in an organ, structure or function (anatomical, physiological, mental or psychological). *The limitation of functional capacities*: compared to a normal social role of an average person in his or her socio-cultural environment, we measure a person's lesser capacity to perform the acts of daily life due to a physical or mental impairment. *Disability* is a phenomenon that takes place in the interaction between a person and his or her environment, this person having a functional or behavioural impairment or deficit; the phenomenon consists in the production of situations of discrimination, marginalization, stigmatization on the basis of the person's differences, or even privilege and power.

> *"Disability is] the effect of the historical normative matrix on the conditions of social participation of different bodies and minds.*
> *This is where the normative discourses and practices that form part of the policies and intervention strategies of the State, interest groups and all social agents come into play.*
> *[...]*
> *The challenge for any different body or mind is to situate its struggle for autonomy within its own norms. And to make it a collective goal..."*
> (Fougeyrollas, 1986)

In September 1995, Fougeyrollas' work resulted in a *Quebec Classification of the Disability Production Process*. The Committee for the revision of the Quebec Classification of the Disability *Production Process* proposal will work from 1995 to 1998 to propose a document to clarify many points of the DPP, notably by giving some definitions, which are listed below.

- An *environmental factor* is "a social or physical dimension that determines the organization and context of a society". It includes social factors (political, economic and socio-cultural) and physical factors (nature and amenities). Environmental factors are measured on a scale ranging from "facilitator" (which favours the achievement of lifestyle habits) to "obstacle" (which hinders the achievement of lifestyle habits), to be understood in their interaction with a person's personal factors (impairments, disabilities and other characteristics).
- A *life habit* is "a current activity or social role valued by the individual or his or her socio-cultural context according to his or her characteristics (age, sex, socio-cultural identity, etc.). It ensures a person's survival and development in society throughout his or her life. The scale for measuring lifestyles ranges from "social participation" to "situation of disability". There are thirteen major lifestyle habits: nutrition, body condition, personal care, communication, housing, travel, responsibilities, interpersonal relationships, community life, education, work, leisure, and other habits. It is within these habits of life that the different situations of

disability will manifest themselves, through changes in social participation.

- *Social participation* is a situation that corresponds to "the full realization of lifestyle habits, resulting from the interaction between personal factors (impairments, disabilities and other characteristics) and environmental factors (facilitators and barriers)". Social participation can be modified by a personal factor or an environmental factor.
- A *situation of disability* corresponds to "the reduction in the achievement of lifestyle habits, resulting from the interaction between personal factors (impairments, disabilities and other characteristics) and environmental factors (facilitators and barriers)".
- A *risk factor* is "an element belonging to the individual or coming from the environment that may cause illness, trauma or any other impairment to the integrity or development of the person". There are four main categories of risk factors: biological, related to the physical environment, related to social organization or related to individual and social behaviours.
- A *cause* is "a risk factor that has actually resulted in disease, trauma or other impairment of a person's integrity or development". Causes are classified on the following scale: predisposing, triggering, persistent and aggravating.
- An *ability* is "the ability of a person to perform a physical or mental activity". There are ten broad categories related to skills related to intellectual activities, language, behaviour, senses and perception, motor activities, breathing, digestion, excretion, reproduction, protection and resistance. Abilities are measured on a scale ranging from "ability" (optimal ability is an intact skill) to "disability" (degree of reduction in an ability).
- An *organ system* is "a set of bodily components with a common function. "There are fourteen major categories of body systems: nervous, auditory, ocular, digestive, respiratory, cardiovascular, hematopoietic and immune, urinary, endocrine, reproductive, cutaneous, muscular, skeletal, and morphological. Body systems are measured on a scale ranging from "integrity" (quality of an unimpaired system) to "impairment" (organic, histological, or physiological damage).

The evolution of the conception of disability in the world cannot be seen in the context of changing ideas about the relationship between man and society. Thus Espring-Andersen (1990) showed that three socio-economic models dominated the world: two based on a face-to-face relationship between the citizen and the state (the British liberal model, the Nordic sociodemocratic model) and a continental European model, which he called "conservative", based "on the variable balance between solidarity (national, family and professional). More recently, however, a fourth vision of the world has emerged, on an international scale and based on the defence of human rights (Roman, 2012). The current understanding of disability is influenced by this new conception of human relations. Thus, we are seeing recriminations by people with disabilities that are manifested at the level of the demand for the equalization of rights and which leads to a different conception of what is still - for want of anything better - called disability.

In this first part devoted to disability, we have addressed the notion of disability, all disabilities combined. We first went through the field of disability in general. First of all, we looked at the origin and history of this notion, then we developed some aspects concerning the consideration of disability. We have focused more on the concept of disability based on the writings of international, European and French bodies. We will keep in mind the ICIDH and ICF nomenclatures that we will find in the third part. We have focused on some of the bodies set up by Law 2005-102, and in particular the MDPH, describing how it works and the tools it uses. We have broadened our scope to include vulnerable people, which includes people with disabilities. Finally, we studied the PPH.

Incidentally, we have seen the term "psyche" appear in the 1988 *International Classification of Impairments, Disabilities and Handicaps,* more precisely in chapter 2, and we have also noticed a clear distinction between "intellectual impairments" and "psychological disorders". This distinction will be adopted, on several occasions, notably by movements that will want to promote "psychic handicap" as opposed to "mental handicap", although this distinction may be subject to debate (Lelièvre, 2006).

The second part will allow us to focus our work on the psychic handicap.

2. Psychic disability

In the first part, we sought to understand the emergence of the concept of disability.
We will advance in our research by studying the recent notion of psychic handicap.
We will have to take up some of the texts already discussed, but go into detail with regard to this particular disability.

We have seen above that the 2005 Law *for Equal Rights and Opportunities, Participation and Citizenship of Persons with Disabilities* gives France a definition of disability and that, for the first time, the possible psychological cause of a disability appears in an official document.
The adjective "psychic" - attested to as early as 1557 - took on the meaning of "which relates to the soul" in 1819, before appearing in 1837 in Balzac's modern sense of "which relates to the mental mind" (Rey, 2010). The noun "psyche" is produced in 1812 concerning a "materialist theory assuming the soul made of a special fluid", and in 1873 it takes on the value of "set of psychic phenomena".
"Psychically" was invented in 1822 by the alienist Maine de Biran. The adjective "intrapsychic" dates from 1907, and describes "what takes place between the elements of the personality". The medical term "somatopsychic" - to be distinguished from "psychosomatic" - dates from 1900 and "concerns both the physical and psychic characteristics" of a person.
Today, "psychic" means "that which concerns the mind, the thought" (Rey and Rey-Debove, 2014).

This part consists of the following chapters:

2.1 Psychiatric disability in France: this very recent term has emerged in the field of psychiatry but has been little used since then, until 2005 when lobbying brought it to the forefront of the French scene. Since then it has become established in the health, social and medico-social sectors. However, this name refers to several meanings based on different theoretical conceptions.
We will go back a few years to study different conceptual approaches.
We will study ways to diagnose this handicap.

2.2 Psychic disability and mental illness: in the related medical-social and health fields, the French particularity of psychic disability is not conceived in the same way. The central question of our work is whether any psychological disability is the consequence of a mental illness.
We will therefore be led to resume a little historical research on the care of the "mentally ill" in order to see the emergence of practices that will allow "mental health users" to emerge.

2.3 Defining psychological disability: we will review the different definitions present on the different media, at various geographical levels in France. We will then take up the notion of mental handicap in an attempt to give a personal definition which, unlike most, will not be correlated to a mental illness and its consequences.
But first, we will have to come back to what is meant by "psychic handicap".
Florence Weber (2016) indicates (2016) that in English *behavioral* and emotional *impairment* - which are often used - are descriptive in nature. Conversely, the French lexicon is imbued with political history and is concerned with the origin of the disorder observed. Thus, in French, *mental* suffers from the ambiguity of being used in association with two names that refer to two different registers, namely "mental illness" and "mental handicap", the first being from the vocabulary of psychiatry while the second is from the field of pedagogy; here we recall the battle between psychiatrists and pedagogues in the 19th century over the educability of idiot children (Fèvre, 2011). The adjective *cognitive* is very recent: "it refers to the scientific and media development of cognitive sciences" (Weber, 2016).

It was in 1937, at the adult day hospital in Vincennes, that the expression "psychic handicap" was first used (Bernard Durand, personal communication, 23 September 2015). From 1952 onwards, the association Croix Bleu-Marine (by analogy with the Red Cross; it later became Fédération Santé Mentale Croix-Marine, then Fédération d'Aide à la Santé Mentale Croix-Marine - FASM) replaced "mental disability" with "handicap due to mental illness", which it had been using until then, but which it ended up finding too stigmatizing.
One of the first measures of guardianship assistance, in a perspective of social and community psychiatry for the mentally ill, can be attributed, in the 1950s, to Pierre Doussinet, chief doctor at the psychiatric hospital of Clermont-Ferrand and member of Croix Bleu-Marine. (Boucherat-Hue and Peretti, 2012). For Marcel Jaeger (2003), it is a notion of the fight against the isolation and segregation of the mentally ill; but it can also be seen as an attempt to bring care policies closer to those of social action: the aim is, from the 1960s onwards, to provide care in the city, with an emphasis on the rehabilitation of patients. Thus we see that the term "psychic handicap" is correlated, in its early days, with that of mental illness.
We will see that it is still the case today in most cases for many authors, but we will show that we can extend it to a whole section of the population which is, in fact, in a situation of psychic disability, without suffering from mental illness.

The notion of mental disability has been constructed empirically, without medical or psychopathological basis (Zribi, 2009). Although Law 2005-102 states that the origin of a disability may be psychological, it does not specify the differences between "mental disability", "psychic disability" and "cognitive disability". Nor does it state that mental disability is a disabling consequence of a mental pathology on the quality of life of the sick, as it seems to be commonly accepted. In fact, by enumerating the possible origins of a handicap, it gives rise to the psychic handicap alongside others, but a definition of the latter could only be deduced by subtracting it from all the others; thus, a psychic handicap would be one that is neither physical, nor mental, nor etc., but rather one that is neither physical nor mental. If this way of defining by saying what is not could be a habit in antiquity, here this method could be applied to each of the handicaps, as long as we are sure that they are all named and exclusive of each other. In any case, this law does not give a definition of psychic handicap and that is why some people try to impose their own definition; and I myself will be led to propose my own. For, apart from the interest of knowing what we are talking about, we will see that, depending on the meaning of the term "mental handicap", the consequences can be very different for the daily life of people in this social situation.

2.1 Psychic disability in France

Contrary to the first part, where we looked at the global, then European and finally national legislative context, we will, in this second part, start from the French point of view, because it appears from the outset that the notion of "psychic handicap" is a national particularity.

Those whom the French Red Cross (CRF) called the "wounded in spirit" - that is, the mentally ill and the mentally deficient - are not concerned by the first law on disability of 23 November 1957: it only deals with physical disabilities. Thus, the hospital takes care of the illness, then the aftercare and rehabilitation organizations deal with social rehabilitation. Lucien Bonnafé and the psychiatrists of Saint-Alban opposed this "separatist conception based on an erroneous doctrinal dualism" by advocating a global approach to the person in his environment.

The psychiatric sector policy implemented in the 1960s offers a variety of care adapted to the case of each patient. It is based on three principles: the recruitment area, responsibility towards the local population and the completeness of the care provided (Hansson, 1996). We have already seen above the 1975 orientation law in favour of disabled persons; it provides them with a status and a guarantee of resources. Those who are disabled by mental disorders are therefore also affected, even if they then appear in the general category of "mental deficiencies". Mental health professionals perceive this law as "illegal", as it does not refer to the psychiatry sector policy. Relying on a 1960 circular, psychiatrists accused the "rogue law" of fixing a person's disability status and, referring to Michel Foucault, of "plunging" a population into a situation of relegation; they remained in their utopia, entering into resistance and assuming their sixty-eight-year-old position as "troublemakers" (Liberman, 2011). In the 1967 Bloch-Lainé report, it is stated that the deficiency at the origin of a disability may be "physical with motor repercussions, and possibly psychic": this is an innovative intuition that will remain a dead letter until the 21st century (Boucherat-Hue and Peretti, 2012).

The decree of 1988, which takes up the work of the *International Classification of Disabilities,* brings out a nomenclature of disabilities, from which I have extracted some passages that concern precisely what could be called - after the law of February 2005 - the psychic handicap. Concerning the deficiencies, a distinction is made between "Intellectual deficiencies" (1.) and "Other psychological disorders" (2.); we also find further on the "Deficiencies of language and speech" (3.). In "Intellectual deficiencies", let us retain the "deficiencies of the course of thought" (18.2) and the "Intellectual deficiency (without other indication)" (19.). In the "Other psychological disorders", we find "Quantitative impairment of consciousness and vigilance" (20.), "Impaired perception or attention" (21.), "Impaired impulses; instinctive behaviour" (22.).), "Disorders of emotion, affect, mood or volition" (23.), "Disorders of psychomotor functions" (24.), "Behavioural disorders" (25.) and "Other impairment of the psyche (without other indication)" (29.). In "Language and Speech Impairments", let us retain "Other Language and Speech Impairments" (38.) and "Language and Speech Impairment (without other indication)" (39.) Let us note that intellectual impairments have been isolated within the impairments of the psyche, that they are the only ones to have been isolated, probably because they are the only ones to have been identified. Within these deficiencies, we can notice some deficiencies that seem to be common to both mental and psychic disabilities (18.2).
Let us now consider the deficiencies of language and speech, and among them we find frequent deficiencies in psychic disability. The text gives a description of the deficiencies, including here the ones I have selected:

> *"« [...]*
>
> *18.2 Impairment of the Course of Thought: Disorder affecting the speed and organization of thought, the ability to form logical sequences.*
>
> *[...]*
>
> *20. Quantitative impairment of consciousness and alertness : (coma; loss of consciousness ..., epilepsy for example).*
>
> *21. Perceptual or Attention Problems: Quantitative or qualitative alteration of attention (e.g., difficulty sustaining attention or misperceptions).*
>
> *22. Impulse disorders; instinctive behaviours : (Anorexia, bulimia, drug use...).*
>
> *23. Disorders of emotion, affect, mood or volition: Disruption in the intensity and quality of feelings, duration, stability of emotional states, ability to engage in intentional behaviour and control one's own actions.*
>
> *24. Psychomotor Function Disorders: Includes disorders ... for an intact motor neurological system.*
>
> *25. Behavioural Disorders: Includes other psychological disorders that could not be classified under the previous headings.*
>
> *29. [...]*

Note. - With the exception of category 20, other psychological disorders correspond to a neuropsychiatric pathology, the breakdown of which into subgroups is given here for information purposes only".

If I underline these different categories, it is because we find them almost thirty years later in what is called today the "psychic handicap".

2.1.1 The Charzat Report

Ségolène Royal - Minister Delegate for the Family, Children and the Disabled - commissioned Michel Charzat to carry out a study "*to better identify the difficulties of people with disabilities due to psychological disorders and the means to improve their lives and those of their loved ones*"; the Charzat report was[35] published in 2002. It reveals that "invisible" disabilities are still very little known by the French population. Indeed, a fixed representation of disability (physical, sensory, mental) obscures the real situations of disabled people and the role of the environment in disability.

> "*...disability is still often represented as a fixed and materialized attribute of the person: the wheelchair, the white cane, or particular facial features.*
> *As a result, "invisible" handicaps remain largely unknown; moreover, it can be considered that this fixed representation, which conceals real situations and the role of the environment, also serves to undermine the approach to "visible" handicaps.* "(Charzat, 2002)

The Charzat report therefore proposes a change in the ways in which disabilities are assessed and the disabled are referred to. The first part concerns the very concept of disability, and very particularly the mental disorders that cause disabilities. The second part of the report deals with the issue of "mental disability", through the difficulties encountered in everyday life: lack of awareness of this disability, fear of illness, stigmatisation of people, their suffering and the heavy burden on relatives. The responses proposed to remedy the situation are the subject of specific recommendations: making an inventory of the existing situation, having it recognised, developing the range of care (psychiatric care in conjunction with social and medico-social care), implementing an action plan for the reception and support of the people concerned, informing the public, training professionals, helping users' associations and family associations, developing study and research programmes, recognising and promoting the power of elected representatives. Let us note the appearance of the expression "*persons in a situation of disability due to psychological disorders*", where it is no longer a question of speaking of "handicapped" but of persons; these are not "handicapped" but in a (social) situation of disadvantage, the latter being due not to an illness, or even a pathology, but to

---

[35] http://social-sante.gouv.fr/IMG/pdf/RAPPORT_CHARZAT_2002.pdf

"disorders", not psychiatric, nor psychological, but psychological. It should also be noted that these psychological disorders are at the origin of disabilities, which we can assume may be specific, as will be indicated by the law of February 2005. We can also note that these handicaps can be said to be "invisible", to be heard in the eyes of the common population; I prefer, for my part, to use the adjective "discrete" because psychological disorders can be obvious to well-informed people. It should also be noted that the role of the environment is recognised as a component of the disability situation, which we do not often find in subsequent texts.

Certain passages of the report are particularly well documented. For example, it is stated that a mental disorder affects the whole personality, not just a part of the person. The causes of mental disability are identified in their diversity: severe depressive disorders, psychotic states, borderline states, age-related mental deterioration, but also those related to intoxications or neurological disorders. The resulting psychological deficiencies are multiple: disorders of thought (delirium), those of perception, communication, behaviour, mood, consciousness and vigilance, sleep, intellectual disorders (memory, attention, judgement, temporal and spatial orientation), disorders of emotional and affective life, as well as the somatic expression of psychiatric affections. The resulting disabilities are numerous in the daily life of people: washing, dressing, eating problems, shopping, cooking, maintenance, travel, administrative and financial obligations, health; they manifest themselves in all areas of social, emotional and intellectual life. This description of mental disability can be used to classify some of the people who suffer from mental disorders. However, the criteria remain imprecise and could be applied - at least in part - to other disabilities or even other vulnerabilities, particularly social ones.

The Charzat report makes an observation: the patient is suffering, but he does not think it is a psychological problem. He recommends that this "denial" be compensated by treatment. As for the latter, an ambulatory system is suggested which operates "24 hours a day in the heart of the city", in order to meet the needs of patients. In addition, he said that patients should be helped to care for themselves, be informed about their illness and be trained to manage it.

We can also find in this report the difficulty of the person "to articulate his or her desire with the reality of the world" that surrounds him or her and therefore the need for care to be based certainly on clinical skills, but also on an articulation between care and daily life, in a relationship of trust and with a formative aim. Another aspect of care concerns the Commune, which is designated to recognize as a citizen the person suffering from mental disorders, particularly in the right to housing, work and leisure.

Finally, in the Charzat report, nothing is said - a priori - about the origin of mental deficiencies in mental disability.

In France, a distinction is made between "mental handicap" and "psychic handicap"; we even know that some associations define psychic handicap in comparison, as opposed to mental handicap. The term "mental handicap" corresponds to a handicap due to an intellectual

impairment, without the origin of this impairment always being questioned. Since the publication of the law of February 2005, the term "psychic disability" has been used to distinguish a category of persons who are handicapped because of "deficiencies in psychic functions". The failure of psychic functions can have multiple causes. It may result from a genetic anomaly, a neurological disorder, a brain trauma, chronic intoxication - alcohol, drugs, medication - or mental illness. It can complicate other impairments - mental, sensory, motor -. It has been found that mental illnesses, commonly known as "mental illnesses", and more recently "psychic illnesses", can have a significant impact on the daily lives of patients; in such cases, they are referred to as "psychic disabilities".
However - in my opinion - mental disability may not be reduced to these cases. It is the social consequences of one or more conditions that constitute mental handicap, and the said origins may be multiple: psychoses, serious depressive disorders, serious neuroses, anxiety disorders, autistic syndromes, frontal syndromes, after-effects of brain injuries, Alzheimer's disease, dementias, etc. If we stick to a definition of mental disability that focuses solely on the social results of a condition - even if unknown - then the meaning of the term can be very broad. If we consider only the consequences of a mental illness, then the spectrum seems much narrower. These two points of view are the subject of lively debate in the various places where mental disability is taken into account, with sometimes sharply contrasting points of view between public health and the medical-social services of associations, among others; but also, within the latter, between those who provide support in finding employment and those who provide support in housing, for example. Moreover, psychological disorders can have very diverse origins. In fact, behind the expression "psychological disability" lies a wide variety of situations and particular difficulties in the social integration of people (Canneva, 2004). However, family members and professionals often agree that a person is mentally handicapped.

We can see that intellectual deficiencies, the consequences of head trauma (cerebro-injuries), epilepsy and autism do not - or no longer - fall into the category of mental disability a priori - because of specific funding, it seems -. Thus, in the scale guide, although epilepsy is classified as a "mental impairment", this category is not included in the "mental handicap" category; nor is autism. Likewise, associations of families of brain damaged people use the term "impairment of higher functions".

According to my experience and in accordance with the discourse of professionals and relatives, three related clinical signs can be highlighted in people with disabilities of psychological origin: procrastination, apragmatism and abulia, these three conditions can lead to inactivity and confinement at home.

- By **procrastination** (from the Latin *pro*, for and *crastinus*, tomorrow) I mean a form of indecision manifested by the frequent tendency to *procrastinate* or even postpone.

- I distinguish by **apragmatism** (from the Latin *a* privative, *pragmaticus* relating to public affairs), the inability to conceive, decide and act, or the inability to coordinate all the partial actions involved in the accomplishment of a task, or the inability to adapt one's behaviour to needs such as the performance of elementary daily tasks.
- By **aboulie** (from the Greek *a* privative and *boulê* will) I name the diminution or deprivation of will, the inability to will or to act, the impotence of action or the desire to act, which manifests itself daily by inhibition.

Moreover, it is also often described in the people concerned a contrast between their potential and their actual activity, their tiredness and slowness, which disconcerts those around them. Abrupt changes in attitude, unpredictable variations in the pace of activity according to the time of day and the day, are also frequently noted.

2.1.2 The CNSA

In accordance with the law of February 2005, the CDAPH may grant to a disabled person who so requests, regardless of his or her disability, a disability compensation benefit, which should enable him or her to achieve greater autonomy.
With regard to mental disorders, this benefit may be granted in three areas: effective assistance from a third party for essential life acts, regular supervision, and additional costs related to the exercise of a professional activity or elective office (Casellas-Ménière, 2006).

I have noted that the PCH "Human Aid" is, in some departments, very restrictive for people with mental disabilities; even if they suffer from apragmatism and abulia, and assuming that the Multi-Professional Team is aware of this, it is not possible to grant them help with household chores for example, which are not considered as "essential acts of existence", without any legal basis.
Moreover, the investigation of the person's application can obviously only take place if the person files a file with the MDPH; for this, the persons concerned must take this first step towards the MDPH. For people suffering from psychological disorders, this act is not obvious. Denial of their difficulties, apragmatism or abuliatism - often described in relation to them - can be major obstacles for some people who cannot bring themselves to take this first step towards applying for help. As the CDM is a one-stop shop, this passage towards it is indispensable; and nothing has been planned in advance to accompany some people in taking this first step. Of course, some MDPHs have learned how to welcome these people with specific needs and expectations; they have set up protocols to reduce the tensions that arise when reception conditions are not well thought out; they have accompanied the reception staff in understanding this public. But some do not make it to the door of the MDPH. We will see further on that a very large number of people in great psychological suffering are unknown to the MDPH, whereas they would be covered by the MDPH under the heading of psychological disability.

Moreover, the constitution of the application file for the MDPH begins with the provision of a medical certificate: in the absence of this document, the file is not processed. I wonder about this obligation, which places disability under the control of medicine. This is no doubt a legacy of the historical conception of the concept of disability, as discussed in the first part of this chapter, but I have seen, on a daily basis, that almost all authors present disability as the consequence of a condition that medicine can describe, or even explain the origin of. Thus, tetraplegia can be explained by an accident, a fracture of the spine and a section of the spinal cord; blindness can be caused by glaucoma, deafness by congenitality. In other cases the condition is found, but its origin is not always known, such as epilepsy, but it can be treated medically. In the case of intellectual disability, apart from cases of trisomy, microcephaly and others, in more than three-quarters of cases, the low intellectual level is noted, or even measured, but no cause is found.

With regard to mental disability, since it is commonly accepted that it is the lasting consequence of a mental illness that affects the capacity for autonomy and adaptation to social life (Pivin, 2006), it seems legitimate to request a medical diagnosis of the illness in question. It should also be recalled that any medical doctor can issue a medical certificate - including a certificate of good mental health - or make a diagnosis of a mental illness. However, I can clearly see in the field how general practitioners are in great difficulty when their patients have mental disorders, and how difficult it is for them to intervene, even if only to renew prescriptions for psychotropic drugs prescribed by psychiatrists. It is they who are asked to provide this first medical certificate. Indeed, the MDPHs cannot require that the initial certificate be drawn up by a specialist doctor, even if some - without any legal basis - do so. And we can see the major difficulty for a person in great psychological suffering, apragmatic or acutely ill, who ends up being able to talk about his or her difficulties to his or her general practitioner to the point of agreeing to conceive that he or she could come under the "Maison des Handicapés", if he or she had to go and see a "doctor of madmen". But let's acknowledge that the doctors of the MDPHs, general practitioners too, without training in psychopathology for the most part, have great difficulty in assessing a person's psychological disability if they do not have, in the patient's file, elements of clinical light.
However, the diagnosis does not bring anything about the singular consequences of a pathology on the daily life of the patient. It is also sometimes difficult to make a firm diagnosis in the psychiatric field, it can take several years; however, even in the absence of a diagnosis, it is quite possible to measure the deficiencies, incapacities and real limits that the disease generates in daily life (Pivin, 2006). Moreover, although mental illness can have social consequences that constitute a psychological disability, if it leads to a real impairment - significant and lasting - of the ill person's capacities, the impact of his or her environment and social outlook on his or her difficulties should not be neglected, which goes far beyond a medical diagnosis.

For my part, I will go even further and say that I do not care what the origin of the disability is, whether there is illness or not. And I will show, later on, that there is not always an illness at the origin of a situation of disability of psychological origin, and that it would be possible to dispense with the medical diagnosis, required at the entrance to the MDPH, if a specialised team were to make an assessment of the situation of disability. Today, the assessment of the person's needs is carried out by the multidisciplinary team of the MDPH. Let us recall that the allocation of the compensation benefit is granted by the CDAPH according to the report of the PE. However, this needs assessment is based on the WHO International Classification of Diseases (ICD 10) which "should be considered by the expert as a basic tool. He will refer to it for the conformity of his diagnostic conclusions" indicates the National Solidarity Fund for Autonomy (CNSA, 2013).

Concerning the psychological deficiencies of adults, the CNSA's guide for[36] CDMs states that

> *"The psychiatric diagnosis does not measure a person's abilities or disabilities in family, social or professional life. The expert will therefore endeavour to supplement the clinical examination leading to the diagnosis with a psychosocial assessment. "»,*

which clearly raises the value of such a medical diagnosis. However, the "expert doctor" is further asked to "globally assess the incapacity according to all the psychological disorders presented by the subject". Thus, the "psychosocial evaluation" - which will make it possible to assess the person's difficulties and thus to recommend compensation - is essentially based on a doctor. It is in fact up to the MDPH PE doctor, qualified here as an "expert", on the basis of a diagnosis made by a colleague, not to take into account only the said diagnosis, but to evaluate a disability, according to the "psychological disorders", by means of a "psychosocial evaluation". The question then arises as to why this assessment task is entrusted to a doctor: in his medical training he has not acquired any psycho-social competence; nor does he have any particular competence either to manage a multi-professional team in a psychosocial assessment. Moreover, we have also seen above that, in the event of an appeal to the TCI, it will still be up to a doctor to assess the person's incapacity.

The multi-disciplinary CDM team has to determine a disability rate for the people who apply to it, and therefore, among them, for those with mental health problems. For a person whose psychological disorders are the main pathology that justifies the request, the disability rate cannot be less than 20%: below this threshold, it is a question of "minor psychiatric disorders", "variations from normal".

---

[36] http://www.cnsa.fr/documentation/CNSA-Technique-eligibilites-web-2.pdf

- If the person "presents psychiatric disorders" but "remain compensated", which "allow a family and professional life assumed alone", then the disability rate will be between 20 and 45%.
- The rate awarded will be between 50 and 75% when "the psychiatric condition requires an adjustment of family and/or professional life with greater or lesser demands from the entourage".
- It will be 80 to 95% when the person "can only live in an ordinary environment thanks to a high level of demand from the entourage" or when "weak and not very lasting spontaneous activity" is observed.

In spite of these recommendations by the CNSA, I have come across cases of people with disability rates of 49% and 79% in particular, who were also reacting violently to the families or the individuals themselves, because this rate excluded them from certain rights, to very little extent, with a sense of injustice and even persecution. Is the purpose of these CNSA indications to avoid hostile reactions? On the other hand, how can it be explained that there are no disability rates above 95%? Furthermore, there is no indication of the means that the PE must have at its disposal to make these assessments. It should also be noted that this guide (indicative of the legal value of a circular, therefore intended for civil servants and not legally enforceable) always refers to "psychiatric disorders" or "psychiatric conditions", whereas this notion does not exist in the guide to scales (legal text). The CNSA thus influences the interpretation of the texts by giving medicine an importance that does not legally appear in them. I would like to point out here that, in the event of an appeal to the Disability Tribunal, only the legal texts will be taken into account, which may explain some rejections of the decisions of the MDPHs. Thus, for example, do the TCIs grant "PCH human aid" to mentally handicapped persons who disagree with the MDPH.

The NFACC guide outlines some of the elements that should be considered when assessing the disability rate. The guide distinguishes between main criteria - which are used to determine a rate of disability - and secondary criteria - which allow a modulation of the rates: relational impact; hospitalizations (recent, prolonged, repeated); the age of the patient, the length of time the disease has been present; treatment -. The impairments are to be looked for in the elementary acts of the person's daily life, and they are listed: toilet, clothing, shopping, cooking, local travel or on a known route; we can now understand why the PCH Human Aid are so restricted concerning this handicap. The main disability criteria considered are volition disorders, thinking disorders, perceptual disorders, communication disorders, behavioural disorders, mood disorders, consciousness and alertness disorders, intellectual disorders, emotional and affective life disorders, and somatic expression of psychiatric disorders. These disorders are discussed in more detail below:

- *Volition disorders* include apragmatism, negativism, obsessive compulsions, ambivalence, inhibition.

- *Thought disorders* (course and content) include obsessive thinking, flight or inconsistency of ideas, slowness of thought, drivel, impoverishment of thought and delirium.
- *Perceptual disorders* include illusions, hallucinations and derealization.
- *Communication* (language) *disorders*, in addition to separately treated aphasia, include disorders of form, language content and gestural expression (logorrhoea, preciousness, donkey cock, neologisms, echolalia, discordance, parasitism, mimicry, gestural or deficient stereotypes) and functional disorders (stuttering, mutism, autistic withdrawal).
- *Behavioural disorders* include aggression; agitation, theatricality, self-harm, phobic behaviour, obsessive rituals, instability, shyness.
- *Mood disorders*, which "should only be considered for disability when they are prolonged (lasting more than six months) or repeated (more than three accesses per year)".
    - *Mild or* balanced depressive or *hypomanic disorders* or well-compensated manic-depressive psychosis compatible with daily and socio-professional life (rate: 20 to 45%);
    - Mood disorders: states of excitement or frank depression without any serious melancholic signs, which nevertheless cause a significant disruption to professional life; daily life is preserved (rate: 50 to 75%);
    - manic state disturbing or hindering socio-professional life: psychomotor agitation, which can be dangerous for the subject and his entourage, flight of ideas, serious insomnia or melancholic state: abuliate, moral pain, self-accusation, psychomotor slowing down, hindering daily life (rate: 75 to 95 %).
- *Disorders of consciousness and alertness,* except for epilepsy treated separately.
- The *intellectual disorders that follow from an early mental illness*:
    - frustrated personality, possibly illiteracy, difficulty conceptualizing and abstracting, but possible adaptation to everyday life (rate: 20 to 45%);
    - possible socio-professional integration in a mainstream environment (sheltered or arranged employment); mild mental retardation [IQ between 50 and 70] (rate: 50 to 75%) ;
    - average mental retardation [IQ between 35 and 49] (80 to 90%).
    - Severe or profound mental retardation, socio-professional integration impossible, language and autonomy nil (rate: >95%).
- Late-onset intellectual disorders include memory impairment, attention problems, impaired judgment, mental arithmetic, and problems with temporal and spatial orientation.

- Emotional and affective disorders include anxiety, anguish, emotional indifference, emotional discord, emotional instability, character disorders, emotional immaturity, shyness.
    - Moderate disorders that do not interfere with social and professional life (rate: 1-40%): permanent anxiety or infrequent anxiety attacks, emotional lability, irritability, shyness, emotional immaturity.
    - Uncompensated disorders that cause significant discomfort to socio-professional life, maintenance of a possible daily life (rate: 50 to 75%): permanent anxiety or repeated panic attacks or significant difficulties in emotional control (in particular frequent inappropriate outbursts of anger, disabling erectophobia), tendency to emotional discordance (unmotivated laughter), poverty of affect, permanent doubt (madness of doubt).
    - Disabling affective disorders or disorders that interfere with daily and socio-professional life (rate: 80 to 90 %.
    - Major affective disorders no longer allowing any contact with reality (rate: 95%).
- The somatic expression of psychiatric disorders: somatisation with subjective complaints without any noticeable impact on daily and professional life, significant systematised somatisation disrupting socio-professional life and leading to a repeated demand for care.
- Serious and disabling alteration of the general condition (e.g. very significant weight loss)
    - hindering daily life (rate: 85-90%) ;
    - life-threatening (cachexia, extensive bedsores, bedridden condition) (rate: > 95%).

Account must also be taken of the secondary criteria which allow rates to be modulated within the bands defined by the main criteria. The following are taken into account: the relational impact on social and emotional life, disorders which may be well accepted by the entourage or, on the contrary, lead to isolation, marginalisation or total dependence; relations with the professional environment, from discomfort at work (but the subject is tolerated by the professional environment) to unfitness for any work; hospitalisations, when they are prolonged, frequent, repeated, may constitute an index of seriousness. The age of the patient and the length of time the disease has been present are to be assessed according to the local possibilities of care.

Let us note these two remarks:

> *"The impact of the various treatments and therapies is not always separable from the pathology that justifies them,*

To be taken into account when this therapy causes discomfort in daily life or regression or side effects for certain drugs. »

We thus have a nomenclature of the *psychological disorders* which must be retained for the appreciation of the *psychological handicap*. It is not indicated how the assessor should proceed: however, I have observed in the field that, when a person presents several disorders among those mentioned above, it is the most serious disorder that is used to assess the rate of disability, which will not surprise us. Although some disorders may be more visible and noisy than others, and the evaluator may choose the one that is the most preponderant and not the one that is the most incapacitating, either in good faith through ignorance or by choice.

If the rate of incapacity of the disabled person is greater than or equal to 80%, he or she is entitled, subject to means testing, to the Disabled Adult Allowance. If the disability rate determined by the PE is between 50% and 80%, the person must prove that his or her inability to access a job is due to his or her impairment: this is called the "substantial and lasting restriction on access to employment", already discussed above. The criteria are specified: "... the *restriction is substantial where the applicant faces, by reason of his or her disability, significant difficulties in gaining access to employment"*. "In a very degraded work context, such as the one we have been living in in recent years, it is particularly difficult to show that the impossibility of access to employment is due to the disability and not to the economic context. The PE takes into consideration the following elements: the impairments at the origin of the disability, the activity limitations resulting directly from these impairments, the constraints linked to the treatment and therapeutic care induced by the disability, as well as the disorders that may aggravate these impairments and activity limitations. A lasting restriction shall be understood to be of a foreseeable duration of at least one year.
It should be remembered that the PE "mobilizes the necessary skills" to make "an overall assessment of the person"; it then presents its conclusions to the CDAPH which, except for the disability rate, makes the decisions.

Annex I of the CNSA guide - which covers all disabilities - sets out the elements for assessing the substantial and lasting restriction on access to employment on the basis of disability. The effects of the disability on access to employment that must be assessed cover both personal factors and factors of external origin. Among the personal factors, the impact of impairments and activity limitations on opportunities for access to employment should be assessed. Among these activity limitations, in addition to those directly related to the pathology, some may have a particular impact on the possibilities of access to employment: these are the activities that appear in the activities, functional capacities section (section 6) of the assessment guide (GÉVA defined by the order of 6 February 2008). We find the activities :

- of the "mobility, manipulation" domain: moving around ;

- of the domain "general tasks and requirements, relationship with others": orienting oneself in time, orienting oneself in space, having relationships with others in accordance with social rules ;
- Communication: conducting a conversation, using communication devices and techniques;
- in the area of "knowledge translation, learning": acquiring know-how, application of know-how.

However, we can note the absence of an "operational definition of disability" (Hamonet, 2010). It should be recalled that it is not indicated what means the PE must have at its disposal to carry out this global evaluation, and that the guide gives a central place for this evaluation to a doctor whose skills do not, a priori, cover this field of expertise. An instruction scheme for RSDAE is proposed at the end of the guide[37].

2.1.3 HEPPAs

Six months after the promulgation of the law of February 2005, associations working on mental disability, satisfied to see this disability recognized, are working to ensure that action on the ground can be effective.

The GALAXIE network (a 2003 association whose purpose is to bring together in a network the ten structures specializing in the field of the socio-professional integration of persons suffering from mental disorders) and UNAFAM (now called the National Union of Families and Friends of the *Sick and* Psychically Handicapped) publish a guide entitled *Specialized Team for the Evaluation of Psychological Disability (E.S.E.H.P.), Specifications*. This tool[38] should enable the assessment of the situation of psychic disability. It recommends the setting up of specialized psychic disability assessment teams (ESEHP) for the most complex cases, and sets out specifications for these teams, which must provide their input to the multidisciplinary CDM teams. The ESEHP is designed to support the CDM PE. The report of its assessment should enable, among other things, the CDM to define human rights in terms of recognition and assessment of disability, assessment of the disability rate and proposed compensation and a subsequent pathway.
The services provided by the ESEHP consist of :

> *"A psychosocial diagnostic service: an expertise allowing the objectification of deficiencies and disabilities characterizing the situation of social disadvantage,*

---

[37] https://www.google.fr/url?sa=tct=j=src=source=webd=1ed=0ahUKEwiu6uio4-3YAhULy6QKHewrDWYQFgguMAArl=http%3A%2F%2Fwww.cnsa.fr%2Fdocumentation%2FCNSA-Technique-eligibilites-web-2.pdfsg=AOvVaw1dP5MVJCYPTNfnTMAM87Ac
[38] http://www.unafam.org/IMG/pdf/2012_Etude_CReHPsy_Rapport_final_Galaxie_Decembre_2012.pdf

allowing social and/or professional orientation in terms of aptitude or incapacity and determining orientation in a protected or ordinary environment;
2. A needs assessment service for disability compensation: this involves determining technical aids, individual or collective human aid. [...] ».

We can see in this text that, as far as mental disability is concerned, we are only talking about adults. This is evidenced by the reference in point II (benefits) to social and/or vocational guidance in terms of aptitude or unfitness and determining guidance in a sheltered or ordinary environment, a reference to the law of 10 July 1987 (on the obligation to employ disabled workers in companies with more than 20 employees) and the absence of reference to the parents of mentally handicapped persons. This does not surprise me too much, given that GALAXIE is a national network to promote the socio-professional integration of mentally handicapped people and that UNAFAM was created by relatives and friends of adults leaving psychiatric hospitals (mostly schizophrenics). We shall come back to the question of mental disability in relation to children and adolescents below.

In a leaflet presenting its action, the Réseau Handicap Psychique de l'Isère (RéHPI), a health network created in 2002 and financed by the Rhône-Alpes Regional Health Agency, has set up an ESEHP; it states that the public concerned consists of "adults in a situation of psychological disability who have a request for professional integration (in an ordinary or protected environment) or for training. "We will also have noted that this system is reserved for "complex cases", without mentioning the criteria for determining these cases. It should also be noted that this specialized team is responsible for "assessing" the disability rate. Moreover, a quick calculation allows us to determine that three full-time people do about 100 assessments each year, i.e. 3 X 152 hours X 10.5 months = 48 hours per assessment on average, over 2 X 5 weeks. Could such an investment in hours currently be made within a CDM EP? Concerning the composition of the specialized assessment team, the specifications are very precise. A professional from the health field is in charge of determining the expression of the disease, the evaluation of the loss of autonomy, the medical feasibility and the validation of the technical recommendations. A psychologist is in charge of evaluating functional incapacities and potentialities, identifying the assets, constraints and maladjustments of the living environment, determining the necessary technical aids, defining the personalised arrangements adapted to the situation, drawing up a list of technical and environmental recommendations, and the technical feasibility of the project. A social worker is in charge of studying and analysing the applicant's situation as a whole, assessing the possibilities of maintaining the person at home or in employment, examining the disabled person's project and his or her priority needs (help in expressing the personal project, assistance in decision-making) and feasibility, and consulting with the various family and other stakeholders (if any). An ESEHP referent is the guarantor of the relevance of the system; he or she coordinates evaluation and expertise actions, and acts as an interface with the CDCPH and the partners concerned.

> *"This team represents, on average, four full-time equivalents to conduct about 100 assessments per year, out of a population of 400,000 people. »*

We can appreciate the details of the composition of the team, and the attributions of each of its members. The presence of a psychologist is particularly noteworthy, without specifying whether it is a clinical psychologist, an occupational psychologist or a neuropsychologist. His tools are not mentioned either. We should also note the "necessary" presence of a "health professional", without specifying whether he or she is a psychiatrist, nurse, nursing assistant or life support worker; however, since "medical feasibility" is one of his or her attributions, we can deduce that he or she must be a doctor. This professional being in charge of "determining the expression of the disease", we can only note that he is thus supposed to be a "disease" at the origin of this psychological handicap. We will see that these questions, which emerge in a text very close to the promulgation of the law 2005-102, will always be present in most of the documents from 2005 to 2015 that we will study in the continuation of this research. Let us finally note, in this small document, some characteristics of the psychic handicap:

> *"... this handicap is characterized by the variety of its individual manifestations as well as by the variability of social and professional efficiency over time"*.

To my knowledge, only one ESEHP was still operating in 2020, namely the RéHPSY health network, mentioned above, and today financed by the Auvergne-Rhône-Alpes ARS and agreed with the Maison départementale de l'autonomie de l'Isère.

2.1.4 The Chossy Report

We have already discussed this 2011 report on disability earlier. It devotes a specific chapter to autism, mental disability and multiple disabilities. One point in this chapter, entitled "Psychic disability *or illness*", states that "The question may still arise as to whether it is a disability or an illness, and the general public's lack of understanding is thus maintained".

Apart from the fact that this is the first time that we have come across the term "psychic illness" in an official text - which was to be used extensively, notably by UNAFAM and the Fondation de France -, there is mention of an "invasive and very seriously disabling disease" which "calls for care" that medicine will "take care of", notably through medication; However, the law of 11 February 2005 recognises as a handicap, which will be "taken into account by the medico-social services", and which requires "empathy, understanding and patience". The report recommends better communication to "demystify mental illness" by raising awareness among the general public, informing families, relatives and the person concerned, and training all those involved. It is necessary to change society's view of this "handicap invisible at first glance", which is surrounded by fear, dread and distress.

The report focuses on the "Psychic Plan" requested by UNAFAM. This plan would recall the need for a specific accompaniment of this handicap because of the denial of the pathology by the person and thus his absence of request. It would recommend a "space" and a legal framework adapted for psychiatry. It would also give an important place to third parties who have to substitute for persons prevented by the disease, and calls for an adaptation and improvement of the existing legal framework, as well as a better knowledge of legal texts. The Chossy report recommends educating the public about mental disability, as well as front-line players (family members, treating doctors, public services), better management of psychiatric emergencies, support for carers, and preventive action to avoid the risk of abandoning people with mental disabilities. The need for "supported housing" to adjust the medical and social pathways is specified.

The Chossy report also makes recommendations at the end. Specific action plans should be updated or created for each type of disability, be it autism, multiple disabilities, psychological disability, sensory, cognitive, mental or other disabilities. Concerning the chapter on Autism, psychic disability *and polyhandicap,* the report recommends support for research in the context of prevention, diagnosis, compensation, support and care. It also recommends "Access to everything for all".

With regard to housing, a change in mentality means that it is no longer possible to envisage immediately setting up specialized structures for the reception and assistance of disabled persons, but that they should be able to benefit, as soon as possible, from services in independent housing. We see the appearance in the city of "supported housing in the diffuse", i.e. housing rented by accompanied disabled persons for access and maintenance in the said housing. Once the real difficulty of the multiplicity of parameters to be integrated to satisfy the housing of a disabled person, according to the nature of the disability, its type and degree, its rhythm and its foreseeable evolution, the lessor has no reason to fear housing it; on the contrary, he has the certainty that an accompaniment at home will prevent all major difficulties. This integration of people with disabilities must lead to a change in mentalities and ensure that future buildings to be built are designed to be practical, safe, comfortable and usable by all, including people with any kind of disability.

According to Stiker (2009), the *psychic disorder was* able to enter the field of disability because of the reduction of symptoms, thanks to psychotropic drugs: a "social and professional reintegration" became possible. At the same time, people can have recourse to *self-care*: within traditional medicine, it can consist of a need for very high-tech care, or self-care; it can also take the form of an address to alternative medicine, to marginal researchers; it can involve recourse to alternative medicine, to treatments administered by non-professionals, which may be religious, irrational, or superstitious. The "psychically ill person" may have a particular relationship to time, with a rhythm of his own that must be respected, an inability to anticipate, to live in the immediate present.

The situation of disability of psychological origin has only recently been recognized, at least in France, in 2005. This notion makes it possible to depart from the medical model of the law of 30 June 1975, which speaks of *mental illness* but not of handicap.

We have seen in some texts some characterizations of mental disability that we will take up again in the continuation of this research, in particular the *Charzat Report*. We also approached the evaluation of this specific handicap, more particularly with the ESEHPs, which we will also find again.
To complete our approach, it is through the psychic handicap seen as the consequences of a disabling mental illness that we are going to approach the psychic handicap.

2.2 Mental disability and mental illness

In the first chapter of this second part, we were able to address the *psychic handicap* which seems to be a French peculiarity.

> *"The concept of mental disability, although present in the terminology of the WHO international models, is only unevenly reflected in the international literature. It is thus absent from the English-speaking psychiatric literature, i.e. essentially Anglo-Saxon.* "(Prouteau et al., 2016, p. 126).

To complete the study of this concept of mental disability, we will look at what are described as the social consequences of severe disabling mental illness. For this purpose, we will resume a historical study of the conceptions of mental illness and its treatment.

2.2.1 Sanitary and Medicosocial

Some authors, in order to describe the characteristics and needs of the general population affected by mental disability, use the French national *Handicap-Santé-Ménages* survey of 2008-2009 as a basis. They immediately come up against a first difficulty: "the lack of consensus on the very definition of mental disability" (Roussel, Giordano and Cuenot, 2014). The categories of activity limitations, impairments and illnesses only partially overlap, not only because of a lack of reliability of the data collected, but primarily because the experience of the very nature of the disability and the qualitative dimension of impairments or activity limitations give discontinuous answers. The data on mental health do not correspond exactly to the expectations regarding mental disability.

In the 1995 law, the legislator introduced three entities that he seems to distinguish: "mental", "cognitive" and "psychic" functions. The 2014 report, on the one hand, refers to the scale guide - derived from the ICF - where disorders are formulated in terms of impairments; on the other hand, it uses the field of the disease - more precisely the ICD 10 - by identifying "psychoses and in particular schizophrenia", "serious depressive disorders and in particular manic-depressive disorders", "serious obsessive-compulsive disorders", by considering them as "disorders causing disability". The report also initially includes "autism and autistic syndromes", "frontal syndromes, after-effects of head injuries and brain lesions" and "Alzheimer's disease and other dementias", which it eventually discards as "the subject of specific public action". We see a threefold movement: the already noted exclusion of autism, head trauma and epilepsy, not because they are not psychological disabilities, but because of more specific funding and support; one reference to ICF in reference to activity limitations and restrictions on participation in social life and another to ICD to delimit the population group. This restriction of the field of mental disability corresponds to the point of view of UNAFAM. This duality of references - fields of disability and illness - has the advantage of homogenising the population concerned. This is how the points of view of UNAFAM and FNAPSY[39] can converge both at the level of individual characteristics and the needs of the target population. For me, this limitation of the field of psychic handicap is artificial, conjunctural. The group in question is part of a larger group of people with a *psychic handicap* (shop)[40]. It is the situation of disability that should concern us, whatever its origin, whether there is illness or not.

The report of the national *Disability-Health-Household* survey states that "about 11.9 million people (including about 10.1 million adults aged 20 and over)" reported "experiencing a disorder or difficulty that could be involved in mental disability". It adds that "the simultaneous declaration of a deficiency in the psychological field and one of the five pathologies mentioned (schizophrenia, autism, chronic anxiety, chronic depression, other psychological or mental disorder) concerns about a quarter of these people, whatever the age groups studied. We can thus see that the fact of referring to both ICF and ICD divides by four the population a priori concerned by psychological disability. This is why I choose not to take into account the origin of the situation of disability of psychological origin but to look for the obvious signs of disability in a population which is not, a priori, concerned by mental illness. However, we must also rely on the work on the fringe of the population that falls within the scope of both the ICF and the ICD, because, in fact, to my knowledge, they are the only ones. The 2005 law, which brought mental disability to the forefront, revealed the housing and independence needs of a whole section of the population. Moreover, it was revealed that 13,000 people in the health field were hospitalized in psychiatric wards for lack of a reception and support solution; in addition, 26,000 children and 11,800 adults with mental disabilities were listed in medical and social institutions and services.

The *Psychiatry and Mental Health Plan* (PPSM) 2005-2008 sought to ensure continuity of care and support for persons suffering from mental disorders, whether they fall within the

---

[39] National Federation of Psychiatric Patients and Former Patients
[40] The acronym is us

health or medico-social fields. This national plan has resulted in the development of facilities for children and adolescents, including medico-psychopedagogical centres (CMPP), special education and home care services (SESSAD) and therapeutic, educational and pedagogical institutes (ITEP). It has also stepped up the provision of medical-social support services for adults with disabilities (SAMSAH), and the sustained development of places in residential care homes (FAM) and special care homes (MAS) for adults with severe mental disabilities. This plan also set up Regional Mental Health Consultations (CRCSM). We can see here a certain continuity between the structures for taking into account disabled persons from childhood to adulthood, from light structures to medico-social devices for more deficient groups. However, I do not find, today, in the field, the feeling of continuity of structures for the medical and social support of people with mental disabilities: there is still a borderline between establishments and services for children and adolescents on the one hand, and those for adults on the other. However, I think that the juxtaposition of these accompaniments may have encouraged the idea of a certain permeability between the health and medico-social fields.

As already mentioned, what is called "the medico-social sector" has no legal existence. The Code of Social Action and Families, since 1975, indicates only "the social and medico-social sector"; it also refers to "social action". Since 1945, the medico-social sector has referred to the elderly and handicapped sector for the people who work there. It is therefore neither medical nor social. I frequently see collaboration between ITEPs and child psychiatry teams; there are also MAS and FAMs that take in patients who have been discharged from psychiatric hospitals. If psychiatric patients become users of medical-social establishments, does this mean that all the users of medical-social structures taking in people with mental disorders are mentally ill? It seems that some people, with a hospitalocentric point of view, think so. Mental illness and psychic handicap would be superimposable. Not only are not all mentally handicapped people mentally ill, but not all mentally handicapped people are mentally handicapped. The fields are related, but they do not overlap. However, we cannot ignore the close links between mental illness and psychic disability, with the reservation that the (medical) diagnosis does not predict the (social inclusion) prognosis, and thus mental illness is not superimposable on disability.

For Yann Boulon and Roger Gayton (2009), concerning people in a situation of disability of psychic origin with psychiatric antecedents, given the non-linearity of the evolutions of mental pathology, the consolidation of the resulting disability is a relative notion. The process of evolution is a characteristic that must be taken into account in any disability assessment process. Any assessment of mental disability must systematically integrate medical and social factors. Situational disability, mental disability is expressed in an environment; the assessment process must therefore be contextualized. Could what seems to be valid for people with disabilities resulting from mental illness also be valid for any person with a disability of psychological origin, including those without a proven mental illness?

2.2.2 Psychic disorders

We cannot miss the term "psychic disorders" that we can sometimes encounter in certain writings. What is the relationship between these disorders, illness and disability? Jacques Sarfaty (2009) states that "mental disability is not to be confused with all mental disorders: it is only one of the socially identified categories". He indicates that what characterizes the psychic disorders of psychic handicap are "the wide dispersion in the level of seriousness of the disorders" and also "a variability or intermittency", the "discontinuity" of the disorders, the "frequent ruptures".

We can thus understand that behavioural disorders - to be understood as manifestations more intense than variations from the normal -, when they have the characteristics listed above, are socially translated into a psychic handicap.

2.2.3 Treatment of mental illness

In order to approach the psychic handicap seen as a consequence of a medical mental pathology, we are going to make a detour through the treatment of mental illness in France.

In this section, we will take an initial legislative and historical approach to the treatment of mental illness in France, and then we will discuss different approaches to current care.

The laws of 1975

Some psychiatrists have relentlessly denounced a certain "*demedicalization of mental illness, experienced as a way of normalizing mental disorders*" (Béliard and Eideliman, 2009).

They thus opposed the policy of the 1975 law on disability, for various reasons: "*feeling of being placed under the supervision of the guidance committees; fear of the dilution of professional secrecy; conviction that assistance only makes sense in the service of care and at the initiative of doctors; the place of families, considered as pathogenic, too important in the text of the law*" (Henckes, 2011).

Some psychiatrists even go so far as to fear for their patients "*being locked into a non-evolving category, as disability is often perceived as a lifelong status*" (Moreau, 2010). In their view, the law in favour of the disabled put their patients at risk of being locked into an exceptional social status, reminiscent of the "incurable" asylums for the insane. (Henckes, 2009).

Within the Croix-Marine Mental Health Federation, psychiatrists were in favour of the recognition of mental disability; the same was true of the presidents of the Medical Commissions of Special Hospitals (Giordano, 2016).

Psychiatrists also opposed the other 1975 law on social and medico-social institutions. This law enshrined a break between the health sector on the one hand and the social and medico-social sector on the other. For them, this went against the spirit of psychiatric sectorization and deprived them of the social destiny of their patients within the city (Henckes, 2009).

The ICF

The ICH had broken the causality between disease and disability. The inevitability of disability was greatly mitigated by ICIDH, which introduced social and environmental factors. Moreover, disability is approached by the WHO with humanistic values that are difficult to oppose; as a result, the theoretical confrontation between psychiatry and the medical-social sector has ultimately weakened (Roussel and Velche, 2011).

The Juppé Ordinance

The Juppé Ordinance of 1996 once again authorizes hospitals to run medico-social services, which they had not been allowed to do since the 1975 Act on social and medico-social institutions. "Some psychiatrists saw this as a regression towards new asylums, places of accommodation without care, for patients who should, according to them, have received unlimited care in hospital. "(Giordano, 2016).
As we can see, whatever the meaning of the legislation, there is still a dispute between the psychiatric hospital and the disability sector.

The Mental Health Consumer Charter

We have to wait until the 21st century for a text proclaiming the right of a mentally ill person to be reintegrated into civil society after hospitalisation. Indeed, it was in December 2000 in France that the *Mental Health Users' Charter was* signed by the Secretary of State for Health and the Disabled, the President of the FNAPSY and the President of the Conference of the CHS CME. This charter guarantees the fundamental rights of psychiatric users: respect for their privacy, their mail, medical confidentiality, etc. Adapted, clear and fair information must be given to them by the carers to whom they owe respect. It lists the bodies that the patient can refer to in the event of malfunctions or to make proposals for improving care systems. *"The mental health user is a person who is not reduced to an illness, but suffers from an illness*. "It should be noted that it is clearly stated that the mentally ill must benefit from social integration and, if possible, socio-professional reintegration in stages that respect the patient's pace and adherence. We can see the appearance in this text of the idea of a return of the sick person to society, without mentioning the notion of recovery, or even consolidation, as is usual in all other medical specialties.
We can see in this text a confusion between health and illness. For my part, I understand "mental health" to mean the state in which an ordinary person is not affected by a "mental illness", with the idea that mental health, like physical health, must be preserved and must therefore be the subject of prevention. I refer readily to traditional Chinese medicine, where a person goes to the doctor to see him or her to keep them healthy; if they are ill, then the doctor

makes a home visit. So a doctor who often goes to the home is considered a bad doctor, because he can't keep his patients healthy, and he loses his clientele. We can see here one of the early models of assessment.

The Piel and Roelandt report

In July 2001, the *Piel and Roelandt report*[41] was made public. The authors, psychiatrists, defend a firm position on the desire to end hospital concentrations in psychiatry. Based on the experience of the hospital of Armentières (North), they propose a territorial organization in order to achieve an articulation between Psychiatry and the Community. The authors talk about the situation of mentally ill people in their care, from the onset of the illness to the social reintegration of the patient into mainstream systems. This report also shows that psychiatrists refuse to confine mentally ill people to a handicapped status. It also clearly indicates the public's lack of awareness of this "invisible disability". A major role is advocated for users on the one hand, and for local elected representatives on the other - especially mayors -.
The 2001 Mental Health Plan (MHP), *The User at the Centre of a Device to be Renovated, is* directly inspired by the Piel and Roelandt report. It should be noted that this report only concerns people with a proven mental illness. The systems put in place tend to restore the person's place in society, despite his or her psychological difficulties.

The medico-social

When referring to the reception arrangements for stabilised sick people leaving hospital, very many psychiatric practitioners often speak of "social", whether they are practitioners in the children's or adult sector; I have been able to observe this on many occasions in the field, constantly since 2008. They seem to be unaware of the term "medico-social", which they understand as "medical and social", for example, for a service the collaboration of a doctor and a social worker. And yet, since the Juppé Ordinance of April 1996, there has been a medico-social sector in the hospital, created following the closure of hospital beds: for example, for psychiatry, Foyers d'accueil médicalisés and Maisons d'accueil spécialisées have been opened, which receive patients with little autonomy, the MAS receiving more dependent persons than the FAMs. Referrals to FAM and MAS are the responsibility of the CDAPH: thus, to leave the psychiatric hospital and join an FAM or MAS, even if the establishment is issued and directed by a hospital centre, the person concerned, in addition to his or her status as a patient, obtains the status of "handicapped person"; as his or her deficiencies are of a psychological nature, the person is therefore psychically handicapped. I think that this hospital-centric vision of the psychic handicap can lead to a lack of knowledge of other less mentally handicapped people. Some psychiatric hospitals have, however, also opened establishments and services for people

[41] http://psydoc-fr.broca.inserm.fr/Professi/Rapports/Piel_Roelandt/default.html

with mental disabilities, which have been called ESATs since 2005, and which employ people who are much more independent than those in FAM or MAS. Other psychiatric hospitals refer their patients to social accommodation structures, either autonomous or semi-autonomous, or accompanied, such as Therapeutic Coordination Apartments (ACT) for example, with continued care. The degree of autonomy of the persons is considered outside their pathologies: while patients may continue to benefit, when they exist, from care in a medical-psychological centre - which is a modality of sector psychiatry -, concerning their autonomy to live in their accommodation, it is the CDAPH that is competent, and it can grant medico-social follow-up such as the intervention of a SAVS or a SAMSAH; these services are financed from the health insurance budget.

General Psychiatry

A psychiatric reference system, published in 2014, integrates the notion of psychic disability (CNUP; AESP; CUNEA, 2014). In this major work co-written by the College of Psychiatric Academics, the chapter on mental disability begins, under the title "WHO Definition of Disability", by giving the French definition of "disability" according to Law 2005-102, which seems strange to me. In the enumeration of impaired functions, "physical, sensory, mental, cognitive or psychic", the last two terms are coloured: while the enumeration may lead one to think that they are different functions, the fact of colouring two of them highlights them, as if they were related, but separates them from the previous one: we saw earlier that the adjective "psychic" was deliberately added precisely to distinguish a specific handicap, which this reference system seems to ignore. In the field, I have often been able to observe that, in the health sector, if there is a clear separation between "mental handicap" and "psychic handicap", the alterations of the psyche are often reduced to those of cognitive disorders. This is, in my opinion, a questionable submission of the psyche to cerebral functions. In fact, from the following point on, the frame of reference differentiates between mental handicap and psychic handicap, in a traditional deficit conception of mental handicap resulting from a "global cognitive deficit leading to diminished intellectual efficiency", and in a description of a "situation of handicap of psychic origin" linked to a "specific cognitive deficit" disrupting activities and social relations; for psychic handicap, it is a "deficiency in the possibility of using one's cognitive capacities". We will note that the psyche is here dissolved in the cognitive. Further on, we find that "*the impairments correspond to the dysfunction of anatomical structures, they include in particular cognitive alterations*". The latter are thus evaluated by "neuropsychological tests". Exit psychopathology. Activity limitation" is defined as "the difficulties a person may encounter in carrying out an activity, i.e. what the person is capable of doing or not capable of doing". In "participation restriction", "it is not about what the person is capable of doing or not doing, but rather what the person actually or effectively does". Participation restriction" refers to "the problems the person may encounter in participating in a real life situation". It can only be assessed "in an ecological way, with the subject in his or her daily life".

I note that this medical book has incorporated the evolution of the WHO's conception of disability. The "management of impairments" is based on "cognitive remediation", which is "similar to rehabilitation techniques" and aims to "reduce cognitive impairments" by "training the impaired processes" or "reinforcing the preserved processes" in order to "compensate for the impairments". Remediation requires upstream a "complete neuropsychological evaluation". The vocabulary "treatment" is still used in the health sector, whereas it has been replaced since Law 2002-2 by "accompaniment" in the medico-social sector. It is still used here, particularly when it is a question of implementing a therapy which, in this work, is of the rehabilitation type, i.e. according to a traditional medical conception of the term, i.e. a reduction in alterations. Thus, even if the term "situation of disability" is used upstream, it is obvious that it is not taken into account in the approach to disability, which remains centred on the person's impairments, whereas it is paradoxically specified that its assessment must be "ecological". The management of participation restrictions is based on "rehabilitation techniques" that contribute to "psychosocial rehabilitation". This passage confirms that it is indeed a rehabilitative approach. The bibliographical references at the end of the chapter consist solely of a book on cognitive remediation of schizophrenia and a reference to the UNAFAM website. This work therefore only refers to a current of thought, predominant in the health sector, of a traditional conception of disability, conceived as a consequence of physiological alterations; however, account is taken of the repercussions of these alterations in the daily life of the person, who is then subject to rehabilitation, according to the WHO medical model.

Rehabilitation

In psychiatry, *rehabilitation* consists of medical, social and educational actions to promote the return of stabilized mental patients to their usual environment, with the best possible level of adaptation. This rehabilitation may begin during day hospital care, in a Part-Time Therapeutic Centre (CATTP), in an aftercare home, and continue in therapeutic apartments, foster care and any ordinary socialization link. Psychiatrists such as Claude Veil and Yves Pélicier were precursors of psychiatric rehabilitation, followed by François Chapireau and Bernard Durand, as a social hygiene or social psychiatry approach, aiming at the social integration of the mentally ill through health actions, the setting up of psychiatric sectors, the use of occupational therapy, "favouring a handicapological approach", even if the notion of handicap still encounters a lot of mistrust from their colleagues (Hamonet, 2010). In English, rehabilitation is called *rehabilitation*.

Psychiatric rehabilitation

Rehabilitation is "a service among other services in a system of organizing care and rehabilitation in psychiatry. "The process of psychiatric rehabilitation helps the person to progress through "a set of phases and activities"; it aims at the "reintegration" of the stabilized patient "into his or her community". It is aimed at people "with a severe and persistent psychiatric disability"; their "psychological disability" refers to "limitations and restrictions on participation" in socio-professional life (Deleu, 2012). The rationale of the Reh@b 2016 congress[42] indicates that

> *"Rehabilitation is a set of tools, techniques, approaches and organized pathways. An organization, an offer of resources, proposed by professionals who listen and respect the users. But it is also, why not say it, as much as a care, a militancy".*

Psychosocial rehabilitation

Psychosocial Rehabilitation was born in the United States of America (USA) after the Second World War. It consists of a social alternative to the dominant medical model in the treatment of psychiatric pathologies. It relies on the strengths of the person rather than on his or her illness to facilitate autonomy within society. This international movement took off in the 1980s, following the deinstitutionalisation movement which, by brutally closing psychiatric beds, left a large number of people suffering from serious psychiatric pathologies abandoned in their families or on the streets. The World Association for Psychosocial Rehabilitation (WAPR) sets out the main objectives and main lines of rehabilitation: the reduction of the symptoms of mental illness and the possible side effects of drug treatment; the development of social skills; the work of providing information and combating the discrimination suffered by people suffering from mental disorders; the organisation of actions around the central place of the user; and the support of families and relatives. "(AMPR, 1996). Psychosocial rehabilitation can be defined as the set of actions implemented to promote the autonomy and independence of people suffering from mental disorders within the community. It involves offering the person à la carte services in his or her environment, combining medical care and social support in a coordinated manner. People are not considered as "sick", but as "full citizens". They should be given a full place within the social space, promote the full exercise of their rights, assert these rights and propose spaces for their effective implementation on a daily basis. Psychosocial rehabilitation is today one of the areas for reflection in terms of mental health policy. It offers specific techniques for accompanying people suffering from severe mental pathologies. The French Committee for Psychosocial Rehabilitation (C.F.R.P.) was created in June 1996.

For Élisabeth Giraud-Baro (2016), psychosocial rehabilitation complements psychiatric care. It must be carried out as early as possible in the course of care in order to limit the development of psychological disability. It consists of an evaluation of functional capacities, the implementation of a treatment and intervention plan, therapeutic education of the person and his or her entourage and cognitive remediation.

---

[42] http://www.rehabilite.fr/p/congres-paris-2016.html

> *"Cognitive remediation interventions play a pivotal role in rehabilitation practice: most of these interventions involve the cognitive processes necessary for, for example, learning, problem solving, self-awareness and awareness of others. Cognitive remediation interventions target "cold" cognitions: attention, concentration, memory and executive functions, but also social cognition. "»* (p. 252)

In order to help the patient adapt to social life, he or she is helped in the hospital to solve problems by training in social skills. The tools used must be transferable to real life. For help in symptom management, stress management, and for the reinforcement of self-esteem, cognitive-behavioural therapies are put in place; they also allow for the reinforcement of self-esteem, self-assertion, metacognition and support of project dynamics.
The rehabilitation path is broken down into programmes such as *Housing first* (social inclusion through housing), *Place and Train* (social inclusion through work). The reference of the path, or *case management,* by coordinating the different actors of the assistance plan, allows an improvement of the social functioning and thus a limitation of the psychological handicap.

Recovery

In English, the term *recovery* could be translated as healing, restoration or recovery of health. The *Recovery* movement emerged in the United States in the 1990s. It denounces the idea that a mentally ill person is doomed to remain mentally ill for the rest of his or her life; instead, they claim the possibility of recovery from mental illness. Recovery suggests that people who are mentally ill have a "favourable future". There is a possibility of "overcoming illness and disability, by re-engaging in an active and social life, restoring a sense of control or taking back control of their lives, without waiting for a complete clinical remission of the illness. "(Pachoud and Plagnol, 2016). Disability is a "temporary situation", it can be transformed, it is possible to get out of it. Moreover, the priority objective is not care, but supportive practices and recovery. The primary goal is not the reduction of disorder, but the support of the progression towards recovery.
Recovery has been inspired by the civil rights movement, but also by the example of self-help groups for recovery from addiction (Shepherd et al., 2008). Those affected no longer want to be just sick people; they want to be recognized as people with a future; no more chronicity, presumed incurability and stigmatization. With regard to recovery, most studies refer to schizophrenia (Pachoud and Plagnol, 2016). However, there are also texts that indicate a recovery from disability: it is a matter of freeing oneself from the disastrous consequences of mental illness and thus, ultimately, of disability.
Recovery involves empowerment, taking control of one's own life. It allows the resumption of activities and the re-establishment of links with others. Recovery must enable the person to manage his or her psychological problems on their own. Recovery allows the person to engage

in valued social roles according to his or her wishes (Slade, 2013). It is a comprehensive - holistic - approach to well-being, built on the strengths of the individual (Davidson et al., 2008). Recovery and psychological disability appear as two opposite poles: the former avoids the latter (Liberman, 2008). They are two processes that confront each other.

The job coaching

In other places, different references to mental disability are addressed by psychiatry; they concern the professional integration of mentally ill people. In this field, recently, job coaching has been on the rise. This is a method of supporting people with mental disabilities within companies. The action consists in designating a support which will make the link between the person concerned and the company to allow the mentally handicapped person to access and remain in employment.

2.2.4 Mental Health

The White Paper for Mental Health

The white paper on mental health, for an association of psychiatric users, carers and social workers in the city, published in 2001, is first of all an inventory, an analysis of the mental health situation in France. For UNAFAM[43] (by its president, Jean Canneva) and for FNA-Psy[44] (by its president, Claude Finkelstein), it is about "making a population exist": people with mental disabilities. First of all, it is necessary to distinguish them from "mentally handicapped" people, suffering from "delay in the development of intellectual functions". UNAPEI[45] (through its president Bernadette Wahl) is in favour of this distinction. The aim is also to rally psychiatric organizations: the French Psychiatric Association, the Psychiatric Union Action Committee, the National Conference of Presidents of Medical Commissions of Specialized Hospital Centres, the Croix-marine Mental Health Aid Federation, the French Psychiatric Federation and the French League for Mental Health. Private psychiatrists and academics are lacking (Chapireau, 2014). Three objectives are announced for people suffering from schizophrenia and delusional disorders :

1. "*to bring the population of mentally disturbed people into the city.*"
2. "to *inform the community about the true nature of this handicap called 'psychic' and the risks associated with it.*"
3. "To *help those responsible for social services in the city and those who are going to allocate available resources and official validations, to ensure that the rights of the people involved are better protected.*

---

[43] National Union of Families and Friends of Sick and/or Psychically Disabled People, www.unafam.org.
[44] National Federation of Psychiatric Users' Associations, www.fnapsy.org
[45] National Union of Associations of Parents, Mentally Handicapped Persons and their Friends www.unapei.org

Claude Finkelstein, in the introduction, reveals:
Page 2

> *"This White Paper has been drawn up by associations of users and carers [...]. They have decided to formalize their partnership in an association called "Santé Mentale France" [...].* »

The association Santé Mentale France (SMF) will come into being in 2016; however, it only includes the FASM Croix-Marine and AGAPSY (a dissident federation of the FASM which will come into being in 2005).
John Canneva, in his foreword, states (page 8) :

> *"The studies currently published in the social field are finally beginning to confirm the need for home-based work. ...] UNAFAM families are also in solidarity with the action of the care teams. ...] The partnership between families and carers, respecting their respective roles, is fortunately a recommendation that is now almost universally accepted.* »

At that time, UNAFAM only knew the mental pathologies of adults, not those of adolescents or children. We can be surprised at the collaboration of families and carers without the participation of the people concerned.
Jean Canneva continues:

> "*...what do we mean by psychic disorders? Behind these terms, which in everyday language can also evoke minor or momentary difficulties, we actually mean serious illnesses that professionals group together under the term "psychoses". We do not think it is useful to be more precise in the context of this dossier, which in fact concerns all psychiatry. ..." (*page 10).

The term 'psychosis' used here is not to be understood in a Lacanian sense of structure, but of proven illness. This position puts aside serious neuroses which can have as a consequence, as we shall see, a psychic handicap. Let us recall that certain serious neuroses are more disabling than certain psychoses.

> "Even if they are not explicitly mentioned here, care for children and adolescents is not forgotten. Accompaniment is just as necessary. The modalities can be adapted from the analyses made for adults. "(page 11).

It is only fifteen years later that UNAFAM will take into account the pathologies of young adults and adolescents.
Alain Pidolle, President of the National Conference of Institutional Medical Commissions (CME) of the Specialized Hospital Centers (CHS), in his foreword, writes :

"The role [of the psychiatrist] in the field of mental health is to organize the system of prevention, care and reintegration of patients.... "(page 14).
The Conference of the Presidents of the CMEs of the CHSs has committed itself, through the "Mental Health Users' Charter" signed with FNAP-PSY, to assist in the development of patients' associations and to help train their members to be effective [within the Boards of Directors of public health establishments and the Conciliation Commissions]. The regulations allowing the establishment of Sector Councils have hardly been followed. ...] Were not minds ripe in 1986 when it was proposed? (page 15).

There is room for patient associations. Psychic disability is seen here only from the point of view of mental illness.
Clément Bonnet, President of the Fédération d'Aide à la Santé Mentale Croix-Marine, in his foreword, writes :

"...] *The notion of accompaniment, which is at the crossroads of various fields: therapeutic, social, educational, legal, is brought into play in a very usual way in the field of mental health. It is, in fact, since the first home visits enabling many psychotic patients to be treated at home or to be able to move into housing, that support practices have developed.*
This philosophy of action in mental health has been carried by the Croix-Marine movement since its foundation in 1952. "(page 16).

We note in this psychiatrist an absence of reference to the medical-social sector which has a long practice of home care.

"« [...]
In other words, Unafam's proposals on the "accompaniment of mentally handicapped people in the city" are in line with the concerns of the FASM Croix-Marine and lead to an active support of all its members [...].
If the law of 30 June 1975, in favour of disabled persons, aroused very strong opposition among psychiatrists who feared that their patients would be labelled with a stigmatising status, the F.A.S.M. Croix-Marine has always sought recognition of the difficulties specific to the evolution of the disease, resulting in certain disabilities.
Thus, many initiatives were based on the Cordonnier law of August 5, 1949 and, subsequently, on the various regulations and compensatory legislation following the 1975 law.
In recent years, the F.A.S.M. Croix-Marine has adopted the concept of "handicap by mental illness". This is a good way of identifying the consequences of the

evolution of mental illness, whether in the register of disability or social disadvantage.
With Unafam, we can now use the concept of mental handicap, which was the one used by Croix-Marine before the 1975 law. (page 17*)*

We see here that "mental disability" replaces "disability by mental illness", which does indeed imply a mental illness at the origin of the disability.

It is, in any case, important to differentiate it from the concept of mental disability, which in psychiatry specifically refers to impairments, generally linked to an alteration of the central nervous system, with motor, intellectual and cognitive repercussions.

We note a classical psychiatric conception of mental handicap that is deficient, far removed from the psychodynamic approach of psychoanalysis, notably in the work of François Sauvagnat and Jean Lelièvre (Lelièvre, 2006).

Behind the psychological disability (characterized by the difficulties of the person who no longer has the capacities or opportunities to participate in the exchanges linked to social life), there is a lack of adaptation and exclusion. Psychological disability means for the person, in any case, a lack of adequacy of the relationship with the environment.
[...]
What is very specific to psychological disability is the need to be able to articulate the persistence of the care dimension and the accompaniment dimension, which is what makes it necessary to overcome the barriers separating the field of care and social life.
[...]
It seems to us more appropriate to speak of community rather than city because it is advisable not to neglect all the actions to be undertaken in rural or semi-rural areas and, on the other hand, the integration process to be supported requires, in our opinion, to be able to rely on community resources, on local communities. This is how the partnership policy should be developed, which must be able to lead to the establishment of functional networks.
[...]
Unafam makes specific proposals to promote the support of people with mental disabilities by recommending, in particular, the establishment of local associative structures acting as resource centres. (page 19).

After a long preamble, the "National Project" is presented on page 20; on page 22 begins an "Introduction: mental health starting from mental disability". We note the use of the term "mental disability" in this 2001 text, which will not be officially accepted until 2005. On page 23, persons with mental disabilities are described as follows:

> "*Observations on the population concerned:*
> *Illnesses of a psychotic nature (mainly schizophrenia and manic-depression) are taken as the typical problems encountered in psychiatry. ...] this choice does not prevent the consideration of other pathologies. It makes it possible to describe the particular nature of the situations caused by these illnesses.*
> *It is with the same objective in mind that we are now being asked to distinguish between mental disability defined by its link with these diseases, and mental disability which, by convention, would be more the consequence of a permanent impairment or a lasting delay in intellectual capacity. The answers to be given in the two cases are, in fact, different.*
> *The psychic handicap... has a destabilizing evolutionary character that remains extremely serious...*
> *The risk of the disease is the same in all countries and in all social and professional environments.*
> *Primary prevention (explaining or preventing the arrival of the disease) is, to date, still very difficult. As we shall see, this has important consequences.*
> *As a result of the reorganisation of psychiatry in France, 80% of the people concerned now live in the city (i.e. outside the hospital).* […] »

We note from the outset that, in the case of "mentally handicapped" people, the discussion immediately begins with a list of mental illnesses; it seems to go without saying that mental disability is linked to a psychiatric pathology. This observation will lead us to a debate that will continue until the end of this book. We also note the wish to distinguish from the outset between mental and psychological disability. We will return to this theme in the next chapter of this work. On page 24, the organizations contributing to this work indicate the partners who must necessarily contribute to the reflection:

> "*The four essential partners:*
> - *The associations that represent user-patients,*
> - *Associations representing users-families,*
> - *Caregiver associations,*
> - *The associations of social leaders in the city.*
>
> […] »

We note that in first place are the associations of representatives of the people concerned, and we see that, fifteen years later, this representation is still not effective in many bodies. We also note that, if the first paragraph indicates "user-patients", it is probably not because we do not want to make a distinction between the client of a medico-social support system and a psychiatric patient; because, if we refer to the second line where it is used "user-families", this shows that families feel at least as concerned by the fate of "theirs" when they are ill as patients themselves would be, and we will see that family associations often tend to take the place of "their children" when it comes to psychological disabilities, or even to consider themselves as their representatives. We also note that between the "carers' associations" and those of the "social leaders" - it is difficult for us to understand who they are - no place is given to the "medico-social" field which, since the post-war period, has traditionally been responsible for supporting the elderly and the disabled. We note that this concept of "mental disability" is hospital-centred, and we will see that it will continue to exist for at least another 15 years.

This white paper has a didactic objective; it wants to make visible an unknown handicap:

> "*Psychic disorder does not necessarily have a visible manifestation. It particularly affects relational abilities and, consequently, one of the major problems of this population is isolation. The resulting loneliness can go as far as the absence of the most basic care, with all the consequences that this entails. There is therefore a vital risk at stake. [...]*
> *In the city, it is not permissible to admit the isolation caused by these diseases. On the contrary, it is necessary to seek to rebuild bonds.*
> ..." (page 29).

Based on the experiences of families and caregivers, society is faced with a major risk for some citizens who break all social ties. In order to make this population visible, a name was necessary: "psychic handicap":

> *"One of the ways to make the population in question exist is to first of all designate it by a name that distinguishes it from other disabilities. This justifies the term "psychic handicap". ...] what characterizes this population is extreme fragility and dramatic isolation.* »

It is a question of making visible a so-called "invisible" handicap, which I prefer to call "discreet" (page 31).
What is the cause of the mental illnesses that cause this disability?

> *"It should be remembered that these diseases occur without known medical causes....* "(page 31).

Thus psychiatry would not know the origins of mental illness. We note that psychiatrists participated in the drafting of this white paper, including representatives of the Fédération d'Aide à la Santé Mentale Croix-Marine.
For a better visibility of this particular disability, it should be clearly distinguished from mental disability :

"In order to distinguish between psychic and mental handicap, there are three possible criteria: intelligence, medicalization, variability. "(page 32).

The definition adopted is as follows:

- *there isn't always a permanent intellectual disability,*
- *there's a behavioral handicap that translates into:*
  - *difficulties in acquiring or expressing psycho-social skills, with attention deficits and difficulties in developing and following an action plan,*
  - *an alternation of calm or tense mental states, which prevent the great majority of patients from assuming a classical professional activity, but which do not exclude a life in an ordinary environment, provided that an adapted accompaniment is instituted.*

We are told that "*the authors of this paper have agreed on [this] text ...*" (page 33).

The three characteristic criteria of mental disability are of different nature. Thus, the intelligence would be likely to distinguish the "mental handicap" from the "psychic handicap", the intellectual deficient thus do not enter the field of the psychic handicap; could this indicate that an intellectual deficient who would contract a mental illness would not be psychically handicapped? We will resume this debate later. Medication would be the second distinguishing factor of psychic handicap. Without psychotropic drugs, no psychic handicap? On the condition that "psychotropic" means "mental illness", which is the only label for "psychic handicap", which raises the question of diagnosis by medication[46]. On the other hand, the variability of the disorders seems to be one of the important distinguishing characteristics identified in people with psychic disabilities, but the causes should be explained.

The consequences of mental disability are well known:

> "*The psychic handicap provokes an "extreme fragility". ...] it is the relational capacities that are seriously disturbed, ... relations with oneself and with others.* "(page 33).

It is astonishing to consider the psychic handicap as being at the origin of the fragility of people: would it not be the opposite, a certain fragility of people would lead them to a situation of handicap of psychic origin; this is what I will support. If relational capacities are disturbed, they put the person in a situation of disability. We can ask ourselves what relationships with ourselves are.

Persons with a disability have the right to compensation for that disability[47]:

---

[46] I personally heard a young psychiatrist, during a synthesis in a psychiatric aftercare centre that I directed in 1996, announce: "*Given the medication he is taking, he is probably psychotic*".

[47] We will find this principle in Law 2005-102 on the autonomy of disabled persons.

"It is practically impossible [...] to try to determine through administrative or judicial procedures, a lasting "right to compensation", which would codify the content of the requested accompaniment according to the situation because [...] compensation is always individual. [...] »
(page 35).
"In order to take account of the nature of the disability, it is proposed that this right to compensation be considered first and foremost as a right to be accompanied and, where appropriate, specifically protected. This accompaniment must be offered and maintained at all times even if the patient denies the illness. Hence the importance of the status granted by COTOREP, which is absolutely essential. "(page 37).

In this text, a reference to the status granted by COTOREP[48] indicates that, as far as mental disability is concerned, only adults are concerned, with children being covered - in 2001 - by the CCPE[49] or the CCSD[50]. This will not be contradicted in the rest of the document.

"To ensure that the right to compensation does not remain theoretical, organizations capable of adjusting the means implemented in practice and over time must be set up.
The issue of housing, which is currently being ignored, must return to the forefront. The deletions of associative flats currently under way must stop. »

An important feature is highlighted here: denial. The mentally handicapped person may sometimes - or even often - be unaware of his or her situation of disability and therefore not want to get out of it. If support is needed, families say that they cannot always provide it, and that the State must take over.
Here we can find an echo of the situation of the insane in the Middle Ages, taken in charge by their families, before the State finally took care of them.
Moreover, concerns about housing are still relevant 15 years later.
Psychiatry is responsible for assessing the needs of mentally handicapped people:

"For medical, psychological and social follow-up to be guaranteed, entities must take care of the population in question and be capable of assessing its needs and adjusting them over time.
This is the responsibility of the [psychiatric] sectors. [...]
If the whole of this population is to be represented, the sectors must be officially recognised as resource centres capable of evaluating all the means to be

[48] COmmission Technique d'Orientation et de REclassement Professionnel (Technical Commission for Orientation and Professional Reclassification)
[49] Primary and Elementary Advisory Commission
[50] Second Degree Consultation Commission

implemented, from accommodation structures for the heaviest cases to home support and emergency facilities.
[...]
The separation of the medical and the social is, in this particular case, impossible.
(page 45).

For the authors of the present proposals, the Sector Councils, as entities of responsibility and consultation, must remain under health control, provided that they are systematically "open" to users and those in charge of social services in the city. »
(page 49).

It is within "Resource Centres" that this evaluation must be carried out. It is remarkable that these centres are given total responsibility for organisation and control, with the condition that they are open to users and to the social sector, while it is specified that the separation of the medical and social sectors is impossible: openness, certainly, but not collaboration. As for the medico-social field, it is still absent.
It is obvious that this is indeed a traditional treatment of mental illness by the psychiatric sector, with an opening to take into account the consequences of the said illness - called "psychic handicap" - for registration in the city. This is in line with the meaning of "mental handicap" as a strict consequence of a mental illness, which seems to me very restrictive and I even wonder about the appropriateness of the term "handicap" in this case.

The Psychiatry and Mental Health Plan 2011-2015

Let us return to the notion of *mental health*. In the *Psychiatry and Mental Health Plan 2011-2015*, the Ministry of Health and the Ministry of Solidarity state that mental health has three dimensions: "positive mental health", "reactive psychological distress" and "psychiatric disorders". Positive mental health aims to improve the development of the individual, and is therefore a discipline that addresses the determinants of health. Reactive psychological distress refers to existential difficulties and distressing situations. Psychiatric disorders correspond to disorders of varying duration, more or less severe and disabling; they require targeted therapies that meet criteria determined by diagnostic classifications.
However, with the WHO, we can take a much broader view of mental health. Indeed, the WHO Constitution defines health as follows:

"Health is a state of complete physical, mental and social well-being and not merely the absence of disease or infirmity. Thus health is not merely the absence of disease.

> *We can also consider mental health as one of the components of health. Mental health is then not just the absence of mental illness. It is, according to the WHO, "a state of well-being in which a person can achieve self-fulfilment, cope with the normal stresses of life, perform productive work and contribute to the life of the community*[51].

For sociologist Lise Demailly (2012), there are also two common meanings of the term mental health. First, the term refers to "being mentally healthy". Second, it also refers to the field of "care of the person," whether psychiatric care or not. It also indicates the recent appearance of "mental suffering": with it, mental health is no longer referred to only mental illness, but opens up to mental disorders in the broad sense, including depression.

Severe and disabling mental illness leads some patients to a situation of mental disability. The treatment of mental illness has been considered to have evolved over the last two centuries. At the same time, the concept of disability has developed. The support of people with disabilities has enabled them to be considered as users of social and medico-social services. Thus, we have seen the emergence of the notion of the mental health user, with an increasingly important participation of the person in his or her care journey. The field of mental health has opened up to mental disorders, and even to psychological suffering. In the field of work, it is questionable whether it also includes Psychosocial Risks (PSR) in the workplace.

Psycho-social rehabilitation seems to be well advanced in Switzerland: there are many reception and meeting places involving local residents, such as the Trajet foundation in Geneva, or the Institut maïeutique in Lausanne, and also the Groupe d'accueil et d'action psychiatrique (GRAP) whose congresses attract many professionals.

Research into mental disability as a consequence of mental illness, especially schizophrenia, is developing, both in psychiatry and sociology, but very little in psychology. Most of this research is Anglo-Saxon and most of the time does not use the concept of handicap (and therefore psychic handicap), or even mention it. This is the case with research on the functional consequences of severe mental disorders, including those in terms of social life (*social outcome*; Smith, 2000; Ridway, 2001; Addington et al., 2003). In France, it is in sociology that the professional integration of psychiatric patients is also widely treated. Thus, for example, the EHESP chair in "Psychic disability and decision-making for others"[52] is headed by Florence Weber, an anthropologist and sociologist, and her team includes many sociologists but no psychologist.[53]

---

[51] http://www.who.int/mediacentre/factsheets/fs220/fr/
[52] École des hautes études en santé publique, Rennes, France
[53] http://www.ehesp.fr/recherche/organisation-de-la-recherche/les-chaires/chaire-handicap-psychique-et-decision-pour-autrui/;

2.3 Defining psychological disability

In this last chapter of this second part, we will seek to produce a definition of psychological handicap that is compatible with the above work and that can be, if possible, commonly accepted.
In order to do so, we will, in a first step, take up different points of view on this singular handicap. Then we will look at four definitions that we have selected because they do not refer to mental illness.

This chapter has the following sections :
2.3.1. **The notion of psychic handicap**: psychic handicap remains a notion, it is not (yet?) a concept. The lack of consensus does not concern the descriptions of the social manifestations of disability but its etiology.
2.3.2. **Definitions** : The lack of etiological consensus should not prevent the search for a shared definition of this notion. We will study four recent proposals for definitions that do not refer to a medically recognized mental pathology. I will propose one of them.

2.3.1 The notion of mental disability

What is psychic disability? Perhaps we could have started with that question.
I preferred to assume that the psychic handicap exists and we tried to circumscribe it. Let us note however that there is no consensus concerning it, neither on the name (psychic handicap, of psychic origin, situation of handicap, shop), nor on its etiology (mental illness, psychopathology, psychic fragility). This is why I will say that the psychic handicap remains a *notion*, in the useful sense of a "still imprecise and vague thought" and not a *concept as a* "constructed and relatively precise representation", of[54] course in the world, but even at the French level. Moreover, I always try to separate this notion of psychic handicap from any medical etiology.

A shared difficulty

It is not only the term mental disability that is difficult to define: it is equally difficult to know what is meant by expressions such as "mental disorder", "mental health problem", "mental pathology", "psychiatric symptoms", etc. It is also difficult to know what is meant by the term "psychiatric disability". (Brossard and Weber, 2016).
These authors point out that, generically speaking, what we are talking about are *disorders* (Emerson and Messinger, 1977). They draw on Mechanic's (1999) work to distinguish between two possible approaches to *mental disorders* by researchers: either we consider that only health

---

[54] https://www.cairn.info/revue-langages-2007-4-page-106.htm

professionals are capable of judging what a mental disorder (a mental disturbance) is, or we believe that a person's entourage may see in him or her a process that leads to a form of transgression of norms that is problematic to the point of requiring psychological or psychiatric intervention.
We are well within this double meaning of the notion of *psychic handicap*: from a medical point of view (consequence of an illness) or from a societal point of view (disturbance of the environment). However, we have seen, further upstream, that the recognition of the status of disabled person by the MDPH necessarily requires the constitution of a medical file with a medical diagnosis. For an administrative recognition of the disability (including mental disability), a medical recognition of a mental disorder is required. For the administration, the mental disability is well constituted of the consequences of mental disorders in daily life. In order to leave this purely medical register, it is necessary to make a detour through the notion of disability as it is read in the theory and history of social sciences, namely "in the increased consideration of the social, material, and symbolic consequences of disorders [...]" (Brossard and Weber, 2016, pp. 186 and 187).

Lack of consensus

We have seen that the notion of mental handicap is a French one, that there is no equivalent in other countries. We have also seen that in France, law 2005-102 - in which the possible psychological origin of a handicap situation appears for the first time - does not give a definition of what is not even designated as a psychological handicap. *The Handicap-Santé survey* carried out in France in 2008 and 2009 - which has already been mentioned - looked at the definition of mental disability. The aim was to define this disability, to estimate the proportion of the French population concerned and to know their needs for help. The lack of consensus on the notion of mental handicap was immediately noticed and posed as an obstacle to the survey, a source of difficulties. Roussel, Giordano and Cuenot, in their analysis of this survey (2014), state :

> *"Analysis of mental health data on illnesses, disabilities and activity limitations shows that there is only partial overlap between these different categories of data.... Nevertheless, the wealth of information collected allows for interesting descriptions of mental health problems, even if this does not correspond exactly to expectations regarding the notion of "mental disability"*.

We will note the lack of consensus on mental disability, which is only a notion, and the meaning of the term *mental health,* which covers both disability and health, the latter with an "illness" component. Above all, we will note that the survey does not produce a definition of mental disability.

Families

The 2001 *White Paper of the partners of mental health France*, seen above, indicates that the people in question present *disorders that are* often variable, intermittent and progressive, that they need regular medical follow-up and that their intellectual capacities are often preserved even if cognitive disorders are often associated. The medical aspect is omnipresent. It is one of these partners, UNAFAM, that takes the torch for the recognition of psychic disability in the law of February 2005. This federation of departmental associations essentially brings together parents of people affected by schizophrenia: these are parents distraught by the sudden appearance of a serious and completely unexpected mental pathology in one of their children. These parents find that once the illness has stabilized, the social reintegration of their child is problematic, if not impossible, and that even continued care is not always assured, that they have to take care of their sick child at home, which puts them in great difficulty. Their main objective - in the recognition of mental disability in the 2005 law - is to distinguish it from mental disability; it seems that they have succeeded in doing so. We note that this distinction is not made in other countries, hence the specificity of mental disability in France.

On UNAFAM's website, it is indicated under the heading psychic disability that its "notion of psychic disability" was retained in the 2005 law, and that it has allowed "sick people and their families" to recognize "illness" and "disability". Then the psychic handicap is immediately differentiated from the mental handicap; concerning the latter, it is indicated in bold "the psychic handicap [is] secondary to the psychic illness"; it is however added that it "remains of unknown cause to this day". Below, however, it is specified that "mental handicap is the consequence of various illnesses": psychoses (and in particular schizophrenia), bipolar disorder, serious personality disorders, certain serious neurotic disorders, but also head trauma, cerebrovascular pathologies or neurodegenerative diseases. Not surprisingly, the link between illness and mental disability is immediately established. We still find this distinction between mental and psychic disability, even twelve years after the law. If its cause remains unknown to this day, the psychic handicap is presented as the consequence of a mental illness or in any case of an attack on the brain. In order to understand what was happening to their children, UNAFAM activists turned to psychiatrists, were trained and acquired a medical vocabulary that they use willingly, although it is not always possible to know the acceptance of the terms used. Medicine seems to exert a certain fascination on the members of this federation; thus, for the symposium of December 9, 2016 on the improvement of the life course of psychically handicapped persons, the ten speakers were doctors[55].

UNAFAM activists say of their mentally handicapped child that "the disease has fallen on them". Then they like to compare the mental handicap to diabetes: lifelong treatment, fluctuations, a disabling illness and no cure. The activists I met have no concept of child psychosis, have no idea of crazy children; they only know about adult mental illnesses, and

---

[55] https://www.youtube.com/playlist?list=PLRER8kCJt0O-Qu8pIa0bMDW4g4-O4oQWl

they speak almost exclusively of schizophrenia and bipolarity. When I ask them about the childhood and adolescence of their child who is now mentally handicapped, they end up recognising some oddities that had not caught their attention, clinical signs that had not been recognised as such; the discussion often ends quickly and abruptly, and I have the feeling of an anxiety that could appear at the idea that, if these signs had been spotted in time, their child would not be in this state today, which seems to be unbearable for them. However, I retain the feeling of a particular fragility of the young person. I have sometimes had the revelation of a particular event that may explain a decompensation, without the parent explicitly making the link between the two.

The other partners in the white *paper are* from psychiatry, both caregivers and patients. Their point of view is hospital-centred and will not be retained here.

The professionals

We have seen that the expression was coined in 1952 within a local hospital structure, namely at the adult day hospital of Vincennes, within the network of the Croix-Marine Federation, in the context of what would today be called "the rehabilitation of mentally ill persons". In this health establishment, mental disability was well seen as the consequence of a mental illness for which the person received care in an open psychiatric structure. The question of the definition of mental disability did not arise at the time, as it was well known that it was the difficulties that people faced in their social reintegration after mental illness. Today, we can see that almost all professionals working in the field of mental disability consider it to be the consequence of a psychiatric illness. This is why professionals in the health field rely on the notion of rehabilitation, and those in the medico-social field on that of recovery.

THE ANESM

In May 2016, the National Agency for the Evaluation and Quality of Social and Medico-social Institutions (ANESM) published a recommendation on the specifics of support for adults with mental disabilities56. The characteristics of the target group covered by this text are set out below:

> *"People's disorders are often variable, intermittent and progressive; they need regular medical follow-up; [...] the situation of vulnerability is permanent even when the disorders have stabilised; people are often unable to ask for help; the invisible nature of the disorders means that the difficulties are sometimes underestimated*".

---

[56] http://www.anesm.sante.gouv.fr/spip.php?article1012ar_mode=calcul

We note that this agency shares the majority view on the need for medical care for people with mental disabilities.

From the beginning, we have noticed differences in the appreciation of what is called psychic disability. We can collect the point of view of the main actors of mental health (legislator, professionals, families). Few actors do not see mental disability as a consequence of a psychiatric pathology. However, we have not found the opinion of the people concerned themselves (the peshops). On the contrary, we can cite the Messidor association[57] in Lyon, which never refers to any pathology whatsoever: it welcomes and accompanies people with their difficulties and their assets, without asking the question of the origin of the handicap. However, all the people received are referred by the Rhône MDPH which, in fact, according to my observations and information, only refers schizophrenic patients to the transitional ESAT. However, I have shown above that it is possible to characterize a psychic handicap without referring to mental illness. Can we go so far as to produce a definition that brings together opinions in this area?

2.3.2 Definitions

In the course of my career, I have been able to meet many players in the field of mental disability, whatever the approach: health, social and medico-social, with a gateway through work or housing, leisure, culture, schooling, care, etc.. I was able to consult many French-speaking websites made by institutions, professionals, psychiatric patients. Most of the definitions that were proposed explicitly referred to mental illness as the origin of psychological disability. In the course of my research work, I have seen many definitions disappear from these sites, without my knowledge of the reason. However, I will now produce four recent definitions of mental disability that do not involve mental illness.
The definitions produced below are from 2014 to 2016. Two have been developed at the level of the Sarthe department, one at the level of the Pays de la Loire Region. The fourth was found in a recent collaborative work.

The definition of ADGESTI

Based on the work of the ADGESTI's multidisciplinary team at its clinical meetings, the Governing Board of this association, at its meeting on 14 April 2014, proposed the following definition:

---

[57] www.messidor.asso.fr

"Psychological disability: difficulty in fulfilling one or more social roles, experienced in the current environment by a person with a psychological fragility, resulting in a restriction of social participation and/or a limitation of activity. »

The professionals of this association, drawing on their experience - notably those of SAMSAH and the Housing Mediation Service - have tried to get rid of any reference to any illness: what is highlighted is a "psychological fragility" at the origin of a current difficulty, experienced by the person and having social repercussions. Thus, going beyond the dichotomy of the diagnosis made either by a professional or by the entourage, and based on clinical signs, it is the person himself who "experiences" a difficulty. In this sense, it is therefore a symptom, in the traditional medical sense of what the person (patient) is complaining about. However, this definition does not take into account denial, which is often described in psychic disability; the person may not experience his or her difficulties, but this does not prevent the disability from arising.

The COHPSY definition 72

In 2014, the Department of Sarthe merged its departmental schemes (child-family, disability, the elderly and integration). On this occasion, public and private teams from the territory's health, social and medico-social establishments and services met around several projects to draw up the action sheets for the future Single Plan. In this context, the aim was to deal with situations of psychological disability. On this occasion, a group called Coordination handicap psychique de la Sarthe (COHPSY 72), tried to characterize the "handicap of psychic origin". Thus the following definition appeared:

"All situations of disability result from the interaction between personal and environmental factors.

Psychological disability is defined as a difficulty in carrying out human activities in one's living environment by a person who has or has had a health problem affecting the psyche and resulting in a restriction of social participation.

The term "health problem" refers to a bio-psycho-social imbalance, in reference to the WHO, for which health questions all the dimensions of a person's life[58]:
Specific health problems include long-lasting (recurrent and variable) and disabling psychological disorders linked to psychological vulnerability or psychiatric pathology.

---

[58] "Health being a state of complete physical, mental and social well-being, and presented as the convergence of the notions of autonomy and well-being".

Human activity" is understood to mean activity that cuts across several fields of competence:

The ability to think, to reason...
The ability to do and act...
The ability to be and exist socially...
The ability to project and invest...

In the context of disability of psychological origin, these faculties may be disturbed, limited or absent, whether or not perceived by the person himself.

Environment" is understood to mean all private and social living environments involving the person: conjugal, family, friendly, rental, professional, cultural, citizen ...
This environment which can be inadequate, helping, rejecting, excluding, valuing, influences the situation of psychic handicap. This situation is aggravated by the lack of knowledge and social representations about people with psychic disabilities.

Disability of psychic origin takes on heterogeneous and very varied situations. Characteristics or constants are observed and stated in various works on the subject. We list them below:

the suffering of the person
the fragility, the vulnerability of the subject
Isolation, breaking of the person's social link
the variability, unpredictability of the disorders
sustainability, evolutionary nature of disturbances
the burden of treatment
the suffering and burden of the family and entourage
Stigmatization, lack of knowledge, fear of the social body

These characteristics of the handicap of psychological origin, imply a global and longitudinal evaluation of the handicap on the four following fields:

Field of cognition
Scope of Technical Capabilities
Social Skills Field
Personal Identity Field

This assessment must be carried out by a multidisciplinary team of coordinated actors from the social, health and medico-social fields, identified in the territory by all the local stakeholders (family carers and professional carers). The aim of this evaluation is to recommend an appropriate orientation and support in order to jointly build a life project.

The identification of the person's disability situations implies recommendations for individualized and adapted support with the need for reassessment.
The finding of a psychological handicap does not exclude the existence of a handicap of another nature (mental, motor...). »

This definition was adopted by the Department of Sarthe in December 2014 as part of the vote on the Single Departmental Plan 2015-2019. Worked by the territorial teams, it wanted to be exhaustive of the vision of the actors concerning the shop. It insists on the interaction between the person and his environment, under the model of the Disability Production Process. It does not refer to an illness, but to "a health problem affecting the psyche". The definition is relatively short (the second paragraph) but the authors felt it necessary to clarify the terms used. Thus, it is specified what is meant by health whose problems, while not referring to an illness, refer to "a psychological vulnerability", but also, and this is not excluded, to "a psychiatric pathology".
The characteristics of the disability situation described are based on work since the Charzat report. The four fields in which mental disability manifests itself relate to the theory of mediation[59]. The evaluation of psychological disability is entrusted to a multidisciplinary team, in reference to the ESEHP recommended in 2008 by the GALAXIE report. The situation of disability is current and evolving. It can occur even in the presence of another situation of disability (therefore mental, for example). This definition, drawn up by the health, social and medico-social teams of the Sarthe region, is now a reference in the region due to its adoption in plenary session by the General Council.

The CReHPsy Pays de la Loire definition

The Sarthean definition of psychic disability was proposed to the Resource Centre for Psychic Disability (CReHPsy) of Pays de la Loire in Angers. It was not retained, notably because of its length. In 2015, the Scientific and Strategic Council of the CReHPsy Pays de la Loire unanimously adopted the following definition of mental disability:

"Disability is not a state of a person's abilities but a situation. The situation of disability of psychic origin is defined by all the restrictions of participation in all

---

[59] See Jean Gagnepain's clinical anthropology, http://www.rennes-mediation.fr/bmedia/articles/la-theorie-de-la-mediation/

areas of civic life linked to a psychic pathology. It can be observed in particular in the fields of daily, relational, social and professional life".

Note the reference, not to an illness, but to a "psychic pathology". The debate revolved around the reference to "mental illness" (the majority view), or a "psychological predisposition" with decompensation (which I defended). The term "psychopathology" - which I proposed - was not retained; the term "mental pathology" was judged too medical; "psychological pathology" was proposed, judged too weak, and finally "psychological pathology" was preferred. This definition fails to take into account who makes the diagnosis of a psychological disability (the person concerned, his or her family and friends, a professional, etc.). It does not say either what characterizes the psychological pathology, nor who observes it. It is this vagueness that allowed the consensus.

A Freudian definition

We have recently found an original definition of psychic handicap, based on post-Freudian psychoanalytical theory (Boucherat-Hue and Brother Artinian, 2016):

> *We propose to take the concept of "psychic handicap" literally... and to define it as a "psychosomatic system of hindrance with dysadaptive repercussions". [...] (p. 360).*
>
> *Its main motor is inhibition [...]. If we want to conceptualize it in psychoanalysis, the psychic handicap could be to the psychic disorder what the character trait is to the symptom [...]. One could say that psychic handicap refers to the social translations of character neurosis, where the symptom refers to the intrapsychic conflict of psychoneurosis. »*

It should be noted that the authors move from the "notion" of mental handicap to the "concept". They refer to a "psychosomatic" impediment in a "character neurosis" whose main disorder is inhibition. It should also be noted that this definition does not refer to an "illness" either, but to a "psychosomatic disorder". We also see that this would not be a symptom. I will not retain this definition in my attempt to develop a consensual definition, as it refers to a particular (post-Freudian) theoretical current.

MY DEFINITION OF PSYCHIC DISABILITY

"The situation of disability of psychological origin (shop) concerns a person with psychological fragility, and who is, moreover, affected by a current psychopathology restricting his or her ability to carry out human activities in his or her usual living environment, in particular to fulfil one or more social roles".

It is by mixing the three proposals developed in the Pays de la Loire region that I can propose this definition of mental handicap. I voluntarily put aside, in this definition, the question of who could make the diagnosis of the shop. I indicated in my research work that it had to be carried out by an ESEHP and I wish that this team could rely on the clinical grid that I elaborated below.

We have retained, in this last chapter of Part Two, definitions of mental disability that do not refer to a mental illness; they are recent. We note that they appear at the same time as other definitions disappear from some websites. These definitions, for three of them, were developed in local contexts. They reflect the point of view of field teams, influenced by the positioning of a departmental association. As we have seen, this association has been offering a welcome and support to people in psychological suffering for more than thirty years, and has implemented innovative actions for peshops. It is from this field experience that its point of view on the shop was asserted. She has succeeded in getting her particular point of view accepted by her local partners.

Ten years after the Disability Act of 2005, which for the first time recognized a disability of psychological origin, a few teams have managed to circumscribe this notion and propose definitions which, unlike those produced previously, do not refer to mental illness as the cause of the disability situation. Thus, we can consider that mental disability, traditionally seen as a consequence of mental illness, is a fraction, a particularity of a larger whole which is that of situations of disability of mental origin. I have therefore been able to propose a broader definition of the Situation of Psychic Origin Disability (shop).

I suggest the setting up of specialized multi-professional teams for the evaluation of the situation of psychic disability (ESEHP) at the level of the departments and I suggest that they use the clinical picture I have developed to recognize that a person is psychically disabled.

We'll find out in the third chapter.

In this second part, we approached the notion of mental handicap as we encountered it in the medical and social field; then we ended with a more traditional approach to mental handicap through mental illness.
Psychic disability being a national particularity, we started its approach in France. We have taken up some of the texts of the previous part, to resume the singular aspects of this handicap; we will retain, in the guide-scale which is used to evaluate the rate of incapacity and the Géva which allows the attribution of the PCH, the description of the particular deficiencies of the psychic handicap.
For our part, we have noted three components of psychic handicap: procrastination, apragmatism and abuliatism. We came back to the functioning of the MDPH and we showed that in all the moments of the evaluation of the handicap and the needs of compensation, a doctor was in place, although his skills do not include, a priori, a knowledge of the psychological handicap.
We have recalled the HSPF study.

At the end of this second part, we can know what we are talking about when we talk about mental *disability*: its inclusion in the concept of disability in general, in that of vulnerability too, its connections with mental illness (or psychic illness, this new name seems to be imposing itself little by little). We have a first description of what this singular handicap covers, at least in its official aspects, and how it can be approached by psychiatry. We have noticed the omnipresence of medicine in the determination of disability, in its evaluation and in care, which may raise questions.
I would say, in fact, that the situation of disability of psychic origin (SHOP) is a singular social situation of a person suffering psychically, and whose characteristics can be determined by a specialized pluriprofessional team (ESEHP) without the need to resort to medicine.
Mental illness can be considered as a degraded situation of a SHOP; the onset of the illness has multiple causes, including the person's environment.
Finally, I regret the general lack of interest of psychologists in psychic disability.

In this second part, we have taken up the numerous descriptions of the manifestations of psychological disability, in different media, and then, from these, a clinical picture of the situation of disability of psychological origin has been constructed.
We have concluded that psychic disability, seen as the consequence of mental illness, is only one of the forms of the situation of disability of psychic origin. We have therefore clearly identified situations of disability of psychic origin without referring to mental illness.
On the basis of this observation, we went looking for definitions of mental disability, and we found four that did not refer to mental illness.
A definition of mental disability was then elaborated which brings together the ideas put forward by those we have retained.

It was then proposed that departments set up ESEHPs for the recognition of situations of disability of psychological origin and suggested that they use the grid that will be presented below.

3. Clinic for Psychic Disability

In the first part, we identified what the concept of disability is, i.e. a restriction of social participation due to health problems, impairments or illnesses, as this concept evolves over time; we were able to see how society could take it into account.
In the second part, we dealt with a specific disability situation - mental disability - and we could see differences in representations, particularly because of the related fields of mental health and mental illness. We showed that this social situation could be measured by a specialized team, without the need to refer to any medical causality. Then we criticized the different definitions of mental disability and proposed our own. Finally we gave the ESEHPs back their honour.
In this third part, we will refocus on the mental handicap in France and we will reveal its main characteristics; we will then propose a clinical picture of this handicap, without reference to a mental illness; then we will present an evaluation grid of the shop. Finally we will suppose a discrete syndrome at the origin of the shop.

This part consists of the following chapters:

3.1 Characterizing mental disability: we will take up the discourse that is held in the field of mental disability in France, particularly in the medico-social sector where the question of mental illness remains underlying, and we will show that our approach - even if it is singular - is in line with current research.
Starting from the diverse but convergent conceptions of the situation of disability of psychic origin, we will be able to establish a clinical picture of this singular handicap by taking up its main characteristics. We will then establish a personal clinical grid of evaluation of the psychic handicap.

3.2 SHOP clinical study: we are going to list all the discourses around the psychological handicap discussed above, and we are going to retain the elements of a psychological nature, leaving aside the sociological aspects, to be understood as the social consequences of the disorders.
We will then produce a clinical picture summarizing the shop.
Then, we will present a practical tool for evaluating the shop in the form of a scoring grid; this allows you to take a photo at a given time, then another one after some time, and then a comparison to measure an evolution, favourable or unfavourable.

3.3 A sidop: we will end this study by posing the hypothesis of a discrete incapacitating syndrome of psychic origin (sidop) at the origin of the shops.

3.1 Characterize the psychic handicap

I have indicated above (part two, chapter 2.1) that I have discovered three clinical signs that characterize a Person with a Disability (peshop)[60]: procrastination (indecision, procrastination, postponement), apragmatism (inability to decide, conceive, act; inability to coordinate a task; behavioural maladjustment to needs) and abulia (decreased will, impotence of desire to act, inhibition); they can lead to inactivity and confinement at home. We will see if this personal observation is shared.

This first chapter of Part III comprises the following sections:

3.1.1 The Versailles colloquium: we will first of all study the writings of a colloquium on psychological disability held in Versailles in 2009. It brought together all the recognized actors of the time in France on research and/or support for people with intellectual disabilities. We will rely on the work reported in the *conference proceedings* (CNSA and CEDIAS, 2009). In particular, we will see a similarity between what is described concerning an experimental device - the anticipation measures of a SAMSAH - and Housing Mediation, i.e. people with psychological suffering and without demand.

3.1.2 The Charzat report: we will take up this document, which explores the field of the autonomy of peshops, their social participation and the quality of their lives: housing, food, resources, participation in social (work, collective actions, etc.) and personal (culture, leisure, social ties) activities.
We will cite other sources - more disparate - from that time and some more current. It appears, in fact, that this colloquium, four years after the law of 2005, continues to be a reference and that the writings produced since then - even those around the tenth anniversary of the law - do not shed any new light, apart from the more recent ones on inclusion in the world of work.

3.1.3 Decisive descriptive elements: we will rely on the elements identified in the first two sections to bring together the descriptive elements of the shops.

---

60 This acronym is from us

3.1.1 The Versailles Colloquium

A national conference entitled *"Disabilities of psychological origin, a shared assessment to better support people's journeys" was* held on 23 March 2009 at the Palais des Congrès in Versailles. The symposium was initiated by a commission from the CNSA to the Centre d'étude, de documentation, d'information et d'action sociale (CEDIAS)[61] to carry out a bibliographical research in France and abroad on the issue of psychic disabilities, to conduct action research and to organize a national symposium.

First of all, Carole Peintre - in charge at CEDIAS - reminds that the expression "psychic handicap" is nowhere defined in a consensual way, including in the legislation, even if it is taken into account in the law 2005-102, which has made this handicap more visible. She indicates that in the course of her research, the expression "Situations of disability of psychological origin" has emerged, particularly in reference to ICF (in a situational approach, disability being understood as an interaction between personal characteristics and environmental factors). Indeed, the environment appears to have a considerable impact on the situation of people with intellectual disabilities, in terms of activity limitations or restrictions on participation. The extreme heterogeneity of the population concerned is due to the diversity of the alterations in mental functions that lead to situations of disability. Needs assessment is a process that must cover all aspects of life, from the person's daily life to his or her housing, working life or schooling (p. 8). To follow Carole Peintre, we use the expression "Situation of disability of psychological origin". We have continued by summarizing this term in "shop" and we have also introduced "peshop" to speak of people in a situation of disability of psychological origin.

Later in the document, concerning the evaluation of the situation of disability of psychological origin, Jean-Yves Barreyre - Director of CEDIAS - states that the person concerned himself must be involved in the evaluation process as an expert: it is he who can explain his relationship to the world. His word, coming from his intimate experience, must be heard (p. 10). For him, the evaluation of shops must be the subject of a dynamic approach, a continuous process, to take into account the variability and unpredictability of events that occur in the life course, and which takes into account the major weight of the environment (p. 11).

Secondly, Claude Finkelstein - President of FNAPSY - believes that it is up to the users themselves and their associations to define their needs. She also hopes that the staff involved will be "professional users" and that training on mental disability will be provided by "user trainers" (p. 21 and 22). We will return to this question about therapeutic education later.

Myreille Saint-Onge - a professor at the School of Social Work at Laval University in Quebec City - tells us that her country has for many years used the following definition of health:

---

[61] http://www.cedias.org/

"The physical, mental and social capacity of a person to act in his or her environment and to perform the roles he or she intends to assume, in a manner acceptable to himself or herself and to the groups of which he or she is a member. »[62]

It acknowledges that it is difficult to apply the principles of the Disability Production Process as an interaction between organ systems (impairments), abilities and environmental factors to mental disability, but it uses the concept of "reduced participation" as an indication of the disability situation. However, if the psychological disorder is "invisible", the manifestations of psychological functioning in a particular environment result in disturbing behaviours to which the entourage may respond in a disconcerting manner and thus invalidate the person's experience; it is then that a reduction in social participation, which is constitutive of the disability, will be constituted. The work therefore consists in reducing the obstacles to "social participation" (p. 57). Similarly, it is by working with the person in his or her environment that a psychologist can address, with the person, the reactions of those around him or her to the manifestations of his or her disorders, allowing him or her to express his or her anxiety and also giving him or her the opportunity to change his or her behaviour to be better tolerated by his or her environment.

Jean-José Mahé shares the experience of the SAMSAH that he directed at that time. He understands by "social roles" those of resident, spouse, worker, parent and citizen. He indicates that it is when a person, because of his or her disorders, encounters obstacles in the accomplishment of these roles - personal and/or environmental obstacles - that he or she is in a "situation of social disadvantage", constituting a disability. Its SAMSAH has obtained from the Sarthe General Council, within the framework of the 2008-2012 departmental plan for disabled people, to be able to intervene with people in difficulty prior to the recognition of disability by the MDPH; this so-called "anticipation" approach, is based on the reality of the difficulty for some people to formulate a request and on the Couty report according to which "in many cases, mentally ill people are not [...] aware of their illness", even if they perceive their suffering. Jean-José Mahé adds: a "spontaneous form of compensation for dysfunctions" in the persons concerned leads to the "invisibility" of this public, whereas this compensation for a deteriorated state of health remains very fragile and can collapse at any time. Most of the time, the underlying problem is only revealed in the "most peripheral manifestations", in difficulties in taking the initiative, for example, or in relational difficulties. The approach of SAMSAH staff is described as "mutual taming", and it is indicated that it requires time: it is necessary to identify and respect the "rhythms of the person's availability". Working with a "person who is not in demand" consists of an accompaniment approach which makes needs emerge and encourages the expression of requests. The living conditions of the person concerned are very

---

[62] *An Act respecting health services and social services,* Quebec, 1991, chapter 42.

gradually modified by "a clinical and caring approach" through interviews and "social and medico-social actions" of proximity.
The incapacity of a peshop is not always visible, but it is experienced by it. An experience of sufficient duration shared with the beneficiary of the accompanying action allows a fair appreciation of the disabilities and an approach of the needs. The evaluation must be "longitudinal, dynamic and participatory". The SAMSAH people followed in anticipation of a move towards the MDPH are described as follows:

> *"...people registered in the pathology, but in such a silent way that it was necessary to wait for a social avatar to reveal this situation. These are people who are often between 40 and 60 years old when we meet them and who have never received care before. Instead, they tend to live in a more or less "homeless" way, but in their own homes, which they eventually own. These are totally silent pathologies. ..."* (pp. 65-67).

Carole Peintre salutes the "avant-garde" and rare position of the General Council of the Sarthe at the time, which allowed SAMSAH to approach people without them having gone through the recent MDPH, whereas - according to her - to be followed by a SAMSAH or a SAVS, "the recognition of disability is a prerequisite as well as psychiatric follow-up"; she recalls that the initial philosophy of these relatively recent services (2005) was precisely "to go ahead of certain requests". The people described are "in a situation of social disadvantage due to psychological disorders", says Jean-José Mahé. The director of the MDPH at the time described the accompaniment as "a process of anticipation in the development of a life project", the latter being the first step required of a person who applies to the MDPH.
Martine Barrès, public health doctor at the General Directorate for Social Action (DGAS), acknowledges that the professionals who refer people to SAMSAH for anticipatory support (social workers, CCAS employees, landlords, etc.) are not often wrong, that "there are not many referral errors", that people are indeed in a situation of disability of psychological origin. It should be remembered that entry to the MDPH for recognition of disability is conditional on a medical diagnosis, and we note that here the situation of disability can be identified by the field actors without the need for any diagnosis whatsoever.
Thus, we can identify two entries for the recognition of a situation of handicap of psychic origin: a scientific entry - stamped by medicine -, and a profane entry which undoubtedly finds its relevance in a statement of exclusion of all other causes of handicap which allows us to conclude that there is a psychic handicap. Let us note that it is a public health doctor who attests to this profane clinic.
There is also the feeling that a part of the population may be in a shop, but that these people will not ask for help, and that it would therefore be advisable that their suffering be identified, and that someone should go and meet them, at home if necessary. Carole Peintre takes up this theme to recall that, if the MDPH is an obligatory passage for the opening of rights to medico-

social devices, another entry door must be proposed to certain people who "do not necessarily have formalized requests". According to her, however, it is necessary to intervene "at the right moment in the person's life trajectory", when they are ready to be helped. She also notes that peshops are currently expressing their suffering in many places, in a kind of wandering, and that they are disrupting all common law systems (p. 72). She thus recommends "listening places" without any administrative procedure upstream, places with free access, "a sort of in-between", which would promote a relationship of trust and which would allow these people to be listened to, accompanied and oriented (p. 73).

This conference shows the relevance of an intervention in anticipation for people without demand, in denial of their difficulties. Like Carole Peintre, I think that places of proximity listening would allow people, feeling the first difficulties because of an emerging pathology, to find psychological help and thus, perhaps, avoid degrading themselves towards a shop.

3.1.2 The Charzat Report

The Charzat report is often cited as a reference, both in the health field and in the medico-social field, as soon as psychic disabilities are involved. We have already studied it beforehand in this book. We are going to take it up again, in more detail, in order to refine the psychopathological clinic of situations of disability of psychic origin.

As noted above, this report was published in March 2002, three years before the Disability Act 2005. In order to draw up this report, a large number of people active in the field of mental health were met, all specialists, in whatever capacity, in shops in France.

> *"...] representatives of associations of disabled persons, patients and families, organisations working in the field of disability, associations of psychiatric carers, and promoters of actions and structures designed to respond to people's difficulties. A number of partners in the work on mental health carried out in the 20th arrondissement of Paris have also been approached. (See list of persons interviewed in appendix 1). "»* (p. 21).

The content of this report thus reflects the social and clinical reality of this disability. We will therefore be able to rely on it to try to identify the specific clinic of the shop. We will thus isolate in this long report the passages where the shops are described. The parts concerned are the following: the "Psychic Handicap": difficulties of daily life. Stigmatization, lack of knowledge, fear; suffering of the person; fragility, vulnerability; isolation, rupture of the social link; variability, unpredictability; durability, evolution; weight of treatments; suffering and burden of the family and entourage (p. 10). It should be noted that this is probably the first time that the term "mental disability" has been used in an official document. It is explained below that the term "mental handicap" is used for the consequences of an intellectual disability, and that it is psychiatric patients' associations and family associations that use "psychic handicap" for the social consequences of "impairments in psychic functions" (p. 26).

In the presentation of the report, in response to the question of the nature of mental disability, a list of mental disabilities is given: disorders of thought (delirium), perceptual disorders, communication disorders, behavioural disorders, mood disorders, disorders of consciousness and alertness, sleep disorders, intellectual disorders (memory, attention, judgement, temporal and spatial orientation), disorders of emotional and affective life, and somatic expression of psychiatric disorders (p. 5). The first disorder (delirium) and the last (expression of psychiatric disorders) refer to an underlying mental illness at the shop; when it comes to characterizing a situation of disability, I set them aside. The others are indeed disorders that may cause a restriction of social participation and thus a situation of disability; however, they are relatively vague, and they could apply to many other situations of disability. Thus, even if this list of disorders may very well concern a shop, even if it is relatively restrictive, it is not sufficient for our research because it is insufficiently precise. Some characteristics of "people suffering from mental disorders" are indicated below: a lack of reference points between their ideas and reality, a lack of means around them; a risk of isolation, a risk of breaking social ties, a vulnerable future, a loss of part of their capacities, an evolution of impairments and capacities (p. 5). Then that the particularity of this handicap is that the person has difficulty articulating his or her desire to the reality of his or her environment (p. 7).

The very broad generality of these characteristics does not allow us to characterize a population: they can concern any socially vulnerable person. The daily consequences of these characteristics, described immediately afterwards, can give us some indication of the areas of daily life in which the impairments of interest to us will appear, although it is specified that other areas of social, emotional and intellectual life may be concerned: washing, dressing, shopping, eating, cooking, maintenance, travel, administrative obligations, finance, health. However, they seem to me to characterize a situation of disability whose approach would be rather sociological. Nevertheless, the report gives us a very clear psychological indication: it seems that the person wants to do, but cannot (p. 7).

Psychic suffering is indicated as complex and difficult to define, and can take intolerable forms without further indication (p. 5). This is to be compared with the fact that the "patient" who suffers does not think that it is a psychological problem, that he is in denial, that he does not realize, or that he does not accept to realize, that "his illness" is of psychological origin (p. 6). The Charzat report warns us that, consequently, the shop will not be easy to perceive and that the person himself will not be of much help to us.

In order to characterise criteria for psychological impairment, the report uses the criteria listed in the *Scale Guide for the Assessment of Impairments and Disabilities of Persons with Disabilities,* which we discussed earlier, and which I shall repeat: volition disorders (inability to act because of an inability to want and decide, negativism, or on the contrary inability to prevent oneself from acting, obsessive compulsions); thought disorders (obsessive ideas, flight or inconsistency of ideas, slowness or impoverishment of thought, delirium); perceptual disorders (hallucinations, derealization); communication and language disorders, autistic

withdrawal; behavioural disorders (agitation, aggression against oneself and others, obsessive rituals, phobias); Mood disorders (depressive disorders or manic states, i.e., states of excitement and psychomotor agitation); disorders of consciousness and alertness; intellectual disorders (difficulties with conceptualization and abstraction, problems with memory, attention, judgment, temporal and spatial orientation); disorders of emotional and affective life (anxiety, anguish, indifference, emotional discordance or instability, character disorders); somatic expressions (somatisation, complaints, alterations in general state). These impairments lead to numerous disabilities in daily life (washing, dressing, shopping, cooking, maintenance, travelling, etc.) as well as in social relations and work. They can be more or less compensated for by the person, with the help of those around him or her, and affect to varying degrees social and professional life as well as personal autonomy (p. 27). We thus read a list of "disorders" - without indicating what is meant by this, without reference to normality - and therefore to variations from normal - or to pathological degrees. These disorders are found in many pathologies and in many situations of disability. Should we ask ourselves how many of these disorders are necessary to characterise a shop?
The Charzat report further describes the social repercussions of these disorders in the daily life of the peshops. They are grouped into five categories: suffering, fragility and vulnerability, isolation and breakdown of social ties, variability and unpredictability, durability and evolutionary nature. Suffering (p. 34): eating and sleeping disorders; deterioration of physical condition; sudden resignation from work, reckless spending; indifference to one's own life, feelings of worthlessness, ideas of death and suicide. Fragility, vulnerability (p. 35): compelling phobic avoidance of anxiety-provoking objects or situations; loss of self-esteem and relationship difficulties; situations of manipulation, abuse. Isolation, rupture of the social bond (p. 35): an inability to decide, to act; inactivity and confinement at home; withdrawal, social isolation; delirium; no longer getting up, letting oneself die. Variability, unpredictability (p. 36): apragmatism, tiredness, slowness in spite of real potentialities; an inability to assume the gestures of daily life; rituals; sudden changes of attitude, unpredictable variations in the rhythm of activity. Durability, evolutivity (p. 36): disturbances over time; significant variations in disturbances over time, by phase; an evolutionary chronicity.

The Charzat report has enabled us to gain a better understanding of the deficiencies of the peshops' psyche and their social repercussions. We note that there is an underlying mental illness.
We will be able to broaden our field of research to refine our clinical approach.

3.1.3 Decisive descriptive elements

If the Charzat report allowed a first work of census of the deficiencies of the psyche of the peshops, other sources allow us either to confirm them, or to refine them: it is about the *white book of mental health* previous to this report, and also more recent texts of professionals or close relations of peshops.

We are going to study the other points of view of this beginning of the century on psychic handicap. We will leave aside the more recent work concerning the employment of people with intellectual disabilities, in particular *job coaching, train and see* and *housing first.*

The difficulty of planning an action

The White Paper of the Partners for Mental Health (2001), seen above, tells us that people with psychically-induced disabilities have severely disrupted relational abilities, both in relation to themselves and to others. Peshops have difficulty acquiring or expressing "psycho-social skills"; there are "attention deficits", difficulties "in developing and following an action plan. "They are extremely fragile and present an alternation of calm and tense psychological states, which does not prevent them from living in an ordinary environment, but on the condition that appropriate support is provided (pp. 23 and 33). This book is a consensus for its authors coming from different worlds (users, parents, staff); it therefore gives relatively vague, general indications that could be applied to other situations of disability. However, we will point out the disruption of inter-human relations and the difficulty in planning an action, which we will find in other authors.

The variability of mental handicap

We find in René Baptiste (2005) that psychological disability can be characterized by psychological disorders:

> *"...] various cognitive or behavioural disorders: fatigability, attention deficits, self-deprecation, demotivation, lack of self-confidence, spatio-temporal confusion, errors in the analysis of the environmental context, mental dispersion, overactivity, cognitive impairment, slowness of thought, loss or disturbance of memory, emotional deregulation,*
> *[...] . "»* (p. 34).

If he indicates that mental handicap is noticeable by its variability over time, the various cognitive or behavioural disorders, as well as by the negative weight of its social representation (p. 36), he does not fail to add, a few pages later, that its "fundamental specificity" is its unpredictability, as much in its occurrence as in its intensity and evolution. Psychic disability is also variable according to each case, depending on the behaviour of the person himself but also of his entourage, and also according to the circumstances. In a word, it is "disconcerting": unlike most other situations of disability, which are fixed, permanent and stable, it is difficult to "measure the seriousness, extent, personal and social consequences" of the shop (p. 47). Baptiste further specifies that its specificity is indeed "the lack of demand, of expression of needs" (p. 61).

The disturbed relationship to time

UNAFAM (2008) states that

> *"The psychological handicap is characterized by a relational deficit, difficulties of concentration, a great variability in the possibility of using capacities while the person keeps normal intellectual faculties.* »

Two characteristics of psychological disability are highlighted: the lack of knowledge, minimization or negation of the disorders on the part of the person himself and/or his entourage; the variability of the disorders and their intensity over time. It is also specified that it is the organization which is concerned: the organization of time, the organization of the anticipation of the consequences of an act, the conception of the reactions of others as well as the possibility of memorization and participative communication. In addition, there is denial, the non-recognition of disorders.

Unafam emphasizes a psychic deficiency that affects peshop and which results in disorders of thought, will, mood, emotional and affective life, awareness and intellectual vigilance, perception, communication and language and behaviour. This impairment translates into disabilities in different areas: the ability to take care of oneself, basic needs, abilities related to housing, training, learning and work.

Relational alterations

Jacques Sarfaty (2009) indicates, in psychic disability, a substantial alteration in a few areas: a restriction of participation in social life (due to poor social and professional adaptation); social skills, those of daily life and autonomy; quality of life (in private and family life); thought and feelings (and as a consequence a modification of self-image, perception, communication and socialization); even cognitive functioning (p.14). He points out that what characterizes psychological disability is a disturbance in relationships; this can lead to chaotic journeys made up of ruptures (sometimes long-lasting or even definitive), feelings of abandonment, loneliness, stigmatization and great precariousness.

Concerning the psychological disorders encountered in shops, Sarfaty describes a "wide dispersion in the level of severity of the disorders", and also "a variability and intermittency" of them; he indicates that "stabilization" can take time. He insists on the "discontinuity" of psychological disorders. For him, a poor family history or mental illness explains the frequency of breakdowns and repeated hospitalizations (p. 42).

Inability to make a claim

The inability of peshops to formulate a request is confirmed by Yann Boulon and Roger Gayton (2009) - from the GALAXIE network - taken in another way, the difficulty to address the MDPH: in the files of request to the MDPH, these people have difficulties "to identify and express their aspirations". The authors recommend a compensation measure upstream of the constitution of the CDM file, or even "work on the expression of the demand" (p. 132).

A singular structure of the peshop?

Yann Boulon and Valérie Deschamps (2009), in their study report on ESEHPs, provide us with a complementary vision of psychological disability:

> *"The fragility of the very structure of the mentally handicapped person leads him to experience the encounter with the outside world at the cost of suffering, as a threat to his integrity. "»* (p. 9).

I wonder about the term "structure" used by these authors, which could imply, in a structuralist psychodynamic approach, that peshops would be of psychotic structure, which, according to our personal observations, does not always seem to be the case.
Boulon and Deschamps point out that peshops, although they encounter significant difficulties in their daily lives, can cognitively show themselves to be "quite effective" in conventional neuropsychological tests. They have also encountered cases of people with significant cognitive difficulties but in massive denial, with the possibility, if psychological support is provided, that they may gradually become aware of their difficulties (p. 59).

The psychological illness at the origin of the handicap

In appendix 4 of its experimentation report on ESEHPs[63], the GALAXIE network proposes an evaluation grid for psychological disability. However, the meaning of the expression "mental handicap" is reduced to a consequence of a mental illness:

> "...*we would gladly say that the specificity of the handicap by psychic illness is precisely the psychic illness.*"

which leads the authors to this conclusion:

> *"There is a fragility in the very structure of the individual, which leads him to experience the encounter with the outside world, at the price of suffering, as a threat to his integrity. "»* (p. 108).

Even if my conception of the situation of handicap of psychic origin is broader than that of the previous authors who reduce it to the consequences of an illness, I share the observation of a feeling of threat of the peshops in their confrontation with the environment.

The unpredictability of mental disability

In the partial report of the CEDIAS action-research (2010) we find an additional indication, from the point of view of support professionals. It is noted the unpredictable nature of behavioural changes, the fluctuation of aptitudes. The services say they have to adapt to the

---

63 https://www.google.fr/url?sa=tct=j=src=source=webd=4ed=0ahUKEwjx49fure7YAhVOyaQKHZX9BucQFghHMAMrl=http%3A%2F%2Frsmy.fr%2Fcontent%2Frapport-expe-prospect-compensation-and-compensation-eval-hpsychic_contents1402998700.pdf&usg=AOvVaw2BvnE2M7cbIDh73P_5Gv0f

rhythm of the peshops, to show "flexibility", even "elasticity". They indicate that any event is a "stress factor, a destabilizing factor", that any unknown situation can generate an unpredictable reaction (p. 77).
I notice here a presentation of the shops on a very loss-making side which clearly evokes psychosis, or even autism, and which could not concern all the shops. What will then be highlighted is the lack of demand for peshops (p.80), which is an obstacle to access to care and its continuity, and also an "inability to project oneself into the future, to take initiatives, to anticipate. »

Difficulties in daily life

A few months later, in the summary of this CEDIAS action-research, it is stated that peshops "have difficulties in implementing everyday acts of daily life" and it is specified that the person concerned may not be aware of his or her difficulties, even though these seem obvious to those around him or her (p. 148). It is also indicated that the difficulties encountered by peshops in carrying out daily activities are related to difficulties in initiating a task (due to lack of motivation) and difficulties in completing the task, even a simple one; it is assumed that it is a different perception of "reality" that is at the origin of these difficulties: it is a question of an apragmatism "characteristic of psychic illnesses", the peshop cannot mentally plan a sequence of actions, even very concrete ones, which "can explain in part the apprehensions caused by the installation in autonomous housing" (p. 148). It is also reported that "psychic illness" disturbs the peshop's inscription "in the usual rhythms of life" and can hinder its spatio-temporal perception.
We will notice that CEDIAS still makes a correlation between shop and mental illness, which seems reductive to me; we will also notice the use of "mental illness" in the singular, a term that could gather all mental pathologies without distinction, as if all could have the same peshop as a common outcome. We will note, however, that what is described as disorders of orientation in time and space is traditionally observed in psychoses. I think that this psychotic disorientation is not found in all the cases of shop, that there are not only mentally ill people, that psychotics are in shop.

Personal hygiene

The summary of CEDIAS' action-research evokes a particular difficulty encountered in shops: personal hygiene. Some peshops are noted to have an "inability to take care of their appearance"; in others, a particular relationship to the body and its maintenance, such as a delay in relation to weather conditions, the wearing of dirty or torn clothing, the lack of taste in clothing. In other cases, isolation can be explained, at least in part, by rejection of others for an unpleasant odour due to poor personal hygiene (p. 149). Here we will recognize the psychotic's special relationship to his body. I remind you that I do not think that it is a question of the totality of peshops.

Housing maintenance

Action research holds the idea that the state of housing often reflects the state of psychological health of the person, and especially its evolution, an idea shared by the SAMSAH psychologists mentioned above. It also indicates that it may be a distinctive signal of a risk of psychotic decompensation. It is often noted that carelessness refers to self-neglect. It is noted that some people do not invest in their home, that there is no photo or object to which the person would be attached, even after twenty years in the same place. There are reports of accumulations of papers and even rubbish cluttering up the apartment, and the impossibility of throwing them away because they act as a barrier to anxiety. There are also reports of homelessness in the home, even if the person is the owner, with significant storage of useless objects (p. 150). The consequences of neglect are odours, fire hazards, water damage or unsanitary common areas. It can lead to conflicts with neighbours, which may even result in eviction. Issues of personal hygiene and housing maintenance are often reasons for involving support services (p. 151). This section is of particular interest to us because it deals with the consequences of the shop and its sociological location.

Relational difficulties

In this action-research, few cases of deviant behaviour such as exhibitionism, for example, are noted. Cases are reported of neighbours' reactions to certain nuisances such as noise, or the fact of staying in the dark, for example. What is striking is the vulnerability of peshops, which leads them to a delicate situation when they meet bad people, when they are targeted by ill-intentioned people, when they are invaded, when their home is occupied by people who racketeer them and lead them into their addictive drift (alcohol, drugs); the neighbourhood can then react with threats and violence (p. 151).

Meals

The preparation of meals is an example of how difficult it is for peshops to take initiative; how difficult it is to decide to go shopping, to fill or empty the fridge, to choose a menu, to cook, etc. (p. 152).

The role of the tenant

The General Inspectorate of Social Affairs (IGAS), in a 2011 report on the "care" of the psychic handicap, gives us its contribution:

> {106} "*The management of mental disability is part of a "process" problem, given its progressive nature, which can vary according to the degree of stabilization of the pathology and the rehabilitation of the person*" (p. 20).

One part of the report deals more specifically with housing: here too there is talk of "carelessness", as an accumulation of objects and waste, with a problem of hygiene and inconvenience to neighbours, and also the intervention of the landlord "on the occasion of acts of routine management". It is recommended, in these cases, "interstitial" solutions to include the peshop in a "global partnership", going as far as "more contented" accommodation solutions ({189}, p. 38). It should be noted that today social workers and landlords increasingly speak of the "Diogenes syndrome" in cases of negligence and accumulation of objects.

The sociological context of work

According to Paul Blanc (1996), behavioural disorders manifest themselves in two types of activities that are difficult to isolate, namely social relationships on the one hand and work relationships that depend on the former. Within the framework of the Obligation to employ disabled workers (OETH), observations are made concerning the situation of disability in the workplace. A few elements can be retained.

First of all, it is recalled that the shop results in "difficulties in acquiring or expressing psychosocial skills". A "deficit in apprehension of reality" may appear in the form of attention deficits, difficulties in developing an action plan and then following it, or in establishing social and therefore also professional relationships (p. 4). In a work situation, this translates into "certain discrete signs" around mood disorders: neglect of clothing, lack of self-esteem, lack of self-confidence, withdrawal, sadness, unpredictability (p. 4). But other signs can also alert, perhaps more visible, such as familiar or saucy words, excessive behaviour, verbal - even physical - aggression towards oneself or others, anger, or even logorrhoea, a misinterpretation of reality, a questioning of the framework (p. 5). The colleagues of a peshop can notice in her psychic register disorders, such as loss of vigilance, concentration, memory and difficulties of reasoning. On the physical level, may also appear fatigue, impatience, trembling, sweating; or loss of appetite, sleep, weight gain, which can also be explained by "the combined and exponential effects of treatments and the taking of toxic substances. "» (p. 7).

For Claire Le Roy-Hatala (2009), an employee is expected to have both "know-how" and "know-how to be". She indicates that it is from the gap between the company's expectations and a person's abilities that disability arises, both in terms of professional and behavioural requirements. What is true for any disability is all the more true in the case of a shop; behaviour affects the register of relationships in general, and the deterioration of certain abilities affects the professional register (p. 111). She cites the work of Pierre Vidal-Naquet (2003) within the Galaxie network, and in particular one of the particularities of the shop, namely "the non-linearity of the disorders" and "the discontinuity of the person's situation", to indicate that the business is destabilized by the evolutionary nature and the "disordered temporality" of the manifestation of the disorders. The firm must deal with the unpredictability of human resources, whereas it must control the course of events and be able to anticipate them in its overall activity. The author recalls the two sides of the underlying mental illness: on the one hand, the chronicity, repetition and recurrence of the disorders, and also the idea of a possible cure, a form of reversibility, or even the disappearance of the symptoms (p. 113).

Let us also remember the considerations on the employability of people with disabilities of psychological origin which are the subject of very recent work; they show that half of schizophrenic people are capable of holding a job in the ordinary work environment, provided that specific support is put in place (Pachoud, 2016).

The psychological characteristics of psychological disability

Gérard Zribi, doctor in psychology, reminds us (2009), as we have seen, that "as with the global notion of disability, that of psychic disability has been constructed empirically, without medical or psychopathological foundation. "He adds:

> *"Psychological disability is not to be confused with all psychological disorders: it is only one of the categories identified socially, in particular by administrative recognition, that of disability"* (p. 14).

Gérard Zribi brings out several characteristics of the shop. First of all, he identifies the areas in which a substantial alteration appears: thinking and feeling (with consequences on perception, self-image, communication and socialization), social skills (autonomy, daily life), social participation - including professional - (through maladjustment), quality of life (private and family) and cognitive functioning. (p. 14). It describes the consequences of these alterations in social life: loneliness, a strong feeling of abandonment and chaotic life courses, with the risk of sometimes long or even definitive breakdowns. He specifies that it is the "disruption of the relationship" that characterizes the shop.

Other characteristics of mental disability

We are going to take up elements seen in the first part of this book to measure if there is a concordance between the descriptions of the main actors of the shop's accompaniment and the official texts, and to complete what has been mentioned above.

The Order of 4 May 1988 *Nomenclature of Impairments, Disabilities, Disadvantages* describes the various impairments encountered in different disability situations. We will only find a few descriptions that may concern the shop as it has just been described. In point 1, impairments, *intellectual impairments, other intellectual impairments,* 18.2 *impairment of the course of thought,* we find a "disorder affecting the speed and organization of thought, the ability to form logical sequences". In point 2, *other impairments of the psyche,* in 21 disorders of *perception or attention*, we note "quantitative or qualitative alteration of attention", and in 23 *disorders of emotion, affect, mood or volition,* we note "disturbance of the intensity and quality of feelings, the stability of emotional states, the ability to behave intentionally and to control one's own actions".

In this nomenclature, only these three deficiencies that can concern the psychic handicap can be identified, including the first one in intellectual deficiencies. This nomenclature is used by

the multidisciplinary teams of the MDPH to recognize a shop. We can see how far away this tool is from everything that could be described above as relating to mental disability and that could characterize it.
In the guide entitled *L'accueil et l'accompagnement des personnes en situation de handicap psychique* (UNAFAM; CNSA; UNA, 2008), we find, in other words, characterizations of the peshop, such as the fact that "At certain times, the person with a mental disability perceives reality in a different way". However, we note an additional indication of denial: "Many people who are obviously concerned may take years to accept the need for care, to mourn their 'old life', or even to seek help. "» (p. 14). In volition disorders, the lack of motivation frequently manifested by peshops, an extreme agitation that hinders action, is noted (p. 16). The guide indicates that people sometimes seem indifferent to their bodies, indifferent to their appearance, that they neglect themselves, that they find it difficult to take care of their health (p. 19). It also indicates a disturbance of the day/night rhythm. There are also reports of cases where the peshop may seem to be living "in a different world", cutting herself off from others (p. 20). The possible presence of "delusions" and "hallucinations" is also mentioned (p. 21). We recognize in the latter manifestations described a symptomatology of psychosis.
Michèle Pivin (2006) indicates some additional elements, linked for her to a psychiatric illness at the origin of the psychological handicap. She thus evokes "the frequent denial of the disease by the patient, and the variations of his state". I note that many writings on mental disability address this particular difficulty of a denial of the pathology in the persons concerned. While I readily admit that denial is one of the characteristics of mental illnesses, especially schizophrenia (but also paranoia and manic-depressive psychosis), I must also point out that what is sometimes described as denial can be a protest by a person who, in a situation of psychically-induced disability, contests an alleged illness assumed by those around him or her, who also want to "lead him or her to care". What is seen as a pathology can also be considered as a variation of the normal.

The *White Paper* - already quoted above - describes an "extreme fragility", a disruption of the relational capacities of peshops, and the constant variability of the manifestations of the disease".
I have already recognized this fragility by including peshops in the group of vulnerable people.

The *CNSA guide* (2013) indicates, concerning the psychic handicap, in the main criteria of deficiency, disorders of volition (apragmatism, negativism, inhibition, but also "obsessive compulsions" and "ambivalence" that we had not met until now); disturbances of thought - both in the course of thought and in content - (obsessive ideas, flight or inconsistency of ideas, slowness of thought, drivel, impoverishment of thought, delirium); disturbances of perception (illusions, hallucinations, derealization); disturbances of communication - language - disturbances of form, content of language and gestural expression (logorrhoea; preciousness ;

donkey; neologisms; echolalia; discordance, parasitism, mimicry, gestural or deficient stereotypes), functional disorders (stuttering; mutism; autistic withdrawal); behavioural disorders (aggressiveness; agitation ; theatricality; self-mutilation; phobic behaviour; obsessive rituals; instability; shyness); Mood disorders (mild or balanced depressive or hypomanic disorders or manic-depressive psychosis, states of excitement or outright depression without serious melancholic signs, a manic state disturbing or hindering socio-professional life (psychomotor agitation, which may be dangerous for the subject and his entourage, flight of ideas, severe insomnia or melancholic state); disorders of consciousness and vigilance; intellectual disorders (memory disorders; attention disorders; disorders of judgement, mental arithmetic; disorders of temporal and spatial orientation); disorders of emotional and affective life (anxiety, anguish, affective indifference, affective discordance, affective instability, character disorders, affective immaturity, shyness) and the somatic expression of psychiatric disorders.

We find here a whole psychiatric symptomatology common to psychotic states, whether or not there is a psychic handicap. There is no denying that they can appear in peshops, those whose psychic handicap is a social consequence of a proven mental pathology, which is not always the case.

A disability and health survey provides us with additional information:

> *"Approaching the notion of mental handicap implies that we also study functional limitations [...] in terms of the ability to concentrate, difficulty in understanding others, endangerment of self, aggressiveness, need for stimulation to carry out everyday activities, difficulty in forming relationships, [...]. "»* (p. 187).

Contrary to the previous point, we note that it is the social situation of the peshop that is put forward, apart from any mental pathology. This illustrates the debate we have been following since the beginning of this research.

With regard to access to employment, we saw earlier that, in order to obtain the AAH, when the person with a disability has a disability rate of between 50 and 79%, he or she must show that he or she has a substantial and lasting Restriction to access to employment. To assess this AHR, the multi-disciplinary CDM team must take into account both personal criteria and factors external to the person. It should therefore assess the impact of impairments and activity limitations on employment opportunities. To this end, the PE relies on the Geva, in its component 6 *activities, functional abilities*. This includes activities in the domain "mobility, manipulation" (moving around); activities in the domain "general tasks and requirements, relationship with others" (orienting oneself in time, orienting oneself in space, relating to others in accordance with social rules); activities in the domain "communication" (conducting a conversation, using communication devices and techniques); activities in the domain "application of knowledge, learning" (acquiring a know-how, applying a know-how). It is clear from this list of activities described above that impairments may appear at each of the levels; however, the PE has no means of assessing them, other than the speech of the person concerned. A peshop may just as well blacken the picture of her situation to the point of no longer being credible, whereas this is her experience, or, on the contrary, in a great denial of her difficulties, undermine the obstacles she encounters and thus disqualify herself, and be considered as "socially handicapped" and not acquire the rights to which she might be entitled. Only a simulation, or - better still - an assessment in a daily environment, could make it possible to objectify the disability.

We have been able to see the different points of view concerning the situation of mental disability since the disability has been recognized in France.
We now have a more precise description of the daily manifestations that we will be able to rely on to characterize shops, but which are both sociological and psychological, and which do not distinguish between symptoms (what the person is suffering from, what he or she is complaining about) and clinical signs (what the clinician sees).
We will therefore be able to make a selection among these elements to retain those that will be useful to us to characterize the shop. From the 2001 *mental health white paper,* through the *Charzat report of* 2002, to 2016, several books have addressed the deficiencies noted by professionals and relatives in people with disabilities of psychological origin. These clinical observations are concordant: they allow us to have a picture of the situation of disability of psychological origin.
However, we cannot be satisfied with this approach. Indeed, the descriptions mix clinical psychological and sociological aspects, impairments and their social consequences.

3.2 Clinical study of the situation of disability of psychic origin

If I take again the indications of the previous chapters, and if I cross them with those above, I can summarize the manifestations of a shop in order to characterize it.

Among the manifestations of the shops, I am going to discard those which, in my opinion, are in the sociological domain. These are the social repercussions of psychological disorders, particularly in housing, training, learning, employment or during collective actions, culture, leisure; they result in a reduction in the person's participation in his or her various social roles (citizen, inhabitant, spouse, employee, parent).

This second chapter of Part III comprises the following sections:

3.2.1 Clinical picture of a situation of disability of psychological origin: I will paint a complete psychological clinical picture that will allow us to characterize the shop.
Then we'll produce a clinical picture of the shops.

3.2.2 Evaluation grid for situations of disability of psychological origin: we will provide clinicians with an evaluation grid for situations of disability of psychological origin (Géshop).

3.2.1 Clinical picture of Situations of Psychological Disability

For the construction of the clinical picture:

1) I counted at the peshops, in the works mentioned above : withdrawal, confinement in the home, social isolation; the inability to stay in one's own home, to organize a social life and leisure activities; fragility, vulnerability, situations of manipulation and abuse; relational difficulties; behavioural quirks and the risk of stigmatization; the suffering of those around them, particularly the family; communication and behavioural problems; aggression towards others; unpredictable, sudden and disconcerting behaviour; lack of lasting relationships; rejection by those around them due to poor personal hygiene; the accumulation of objects and complaints from the entourage; the lack of maintenance of the home and complaints from the environment; inappropriate reactions through misinterpretation of behaviour, speech or looks; exaggerated susceptibility; hypersensitivity to family events; a constant need for stimulation; difficulty in forming relationships; inability to carry out an activity; difficulties in being within the norm; difficulties in complying with the rules of everyday life; disruption of common law arrangements; lack of social participation; breakdown of social ties.

2) I have taken into account that the psychological disorders described in the shops are found in all spheres of daily life:

- Ensure basic needs (food, protection, resources),
- Take care of yourself (health, grooming, clothing),
- Living in one's home (maintenance of premises, purchases),
- Have a civic life (administrative procedures).

3) I have also taken into account that the main characteristics of these disorders are variability over time, unpredictability, evolutionary phases, durability and possible chronicization, with most of the time intellectual faculties being maintained.
I have grouped, in descending order of characterization, the identified shop specificity disorders into eleven families, and I have thus been able to elaborate my clinical picture of the following shops.

This table also includes what we have identified as the main characteristics of the shops, in addition to being more complete.

If we go back to my first approach to the shops, we will find in this clinical picture below a kinship with volition disorders - which I have chosen to put in first place -: the lack of initiative with **procrastination**; **apragmatism**; the inability to decide and act with **abulia**.

CLINICAL PICTURE OF SITUATIONS OF DISABILITY OF PSYCHIC ORIGIN

1. **Volition disorder**:
    a. no initiative
    b. apragmatism, inability to act due to an inability to will
    c. inability to cope with the gestures of daily life by :
        i. failure to decide
        ii. failure to act
    d. inability to stop acting, compulsive acts

2. **Disturbance of consciousness and alertness**:
    a. lack of awareness
    b. lack of expression of needs
    c. not being able to apply for help

3. **Mood disorders**:
    a. low self-esteem
    b. negativism
    c. depressive disorders
    d. hypomaniacal behaviour

4. **Psychic suffering**:
    a. sadness
    b. low self-esteem
    c. demotivation
    d. stress hypersensitivity
    e. feeling of worthlessness
    f. use of alcohol or cannabis
    g. silent inscription in the pathology
    h. indifference to one's own life, letting oneself die...
    i. thoughts of death and suicide

5. **Thought disorder**:
    a. slowness or impoverishment of thought
    b. denial of disease
    c. flight or inconsistency of ideas
    d. haunting thoughts
    e. delirium

6. **Somatic Expressions** :
    a. fatigability
    b. slow despite real potential
    c. psychomotor agitation
    d. sensory hypersensitivity (visual, auditory)
    e. somatizations
    f. physical degradation
    g. deterioration in general condition

7. **Intellectual disorders**:
    a. attention deficit
    b. difficulties of conceptualization and abstraction
    c. ADHD
    d. memory disorders
    e. disturbances of temporal and spatial orientation
    f. lack of analysis of the environmental context
    g. inability to foresee the consequences of an act
    h. impaired judgement

8. **Emotional Life Disorders**:
    a. emotional deregulation
    b. indifference
    c. anxiety
    d. anguish

9. **Emotional Life Disorders** :
    a. relationship problems
    b. emotional discord or instability
    c. character disorders

10. **Behavioural disorders**:
    a. agitation
    b. overactivity
    c. aggressiveness
    d. difficulty in following the rules
    e. sudden changes in attitude, unpredictability
    f. invasion
    g. sleep problems
    h. eating disorders

i. rituals
j. phobic avoidance of objects or anxiety-provoking situations
k. hoarding
l. incurie
m. wandering

11. **Perceptual disorders** :
   a. hallucinations,
   b. derealization.

Éric FÈVRE, 2017

3.2.2 Evaluation Grid for Situations of Psychic Disability

Starting from this clinical picture, an observation makes it possible to draw up a table of the difficulties encountered by the peshop and to work out an adapted singular compensation plan.

The Disability Act 2005 is based on the ICF (WHO) and states that disability has three dimensions: impairments (D), activity limitations (LA) and participation restrictions (RP), "modulated by personal and environmental factors". An evaluation of a shop should therefore focus on each of these three areas. Cognitive skills and impairments (D) and their use in various tasks of daily living are captured by neuropsychological assessments. The ability to assess skills, particularly cognitive skills in tasks of daily living, are the subject of occupational therapy assessments. A psychological assessment will look at personal factors (PF) and environmental factors (EF). The latter will also be studied by social workers, system specialists, etc. (Prouteau et al., 2016).
Local practices diverge regarding the objectification of LAs and PRs in the field; while LAs are better taken into account over time, the evaluation of PRs seems insufficient, especially when it comes to compensating for the handicap (Belio, 2012). However, we are seeing the emergence of *performance-based* instruments, real *world* functioning (Bowie et al., 2008). It is by taking these approaches into account that we have continued our work.

From the clinical picture of the situations of disability of psychic origin that we have established, we have been able to elaborate an **Evaluation Grid of the situation of disability of psychic origin (Géshop) in order to be** able to measure the degree of psychic disability of a person at a given moment. The interest of this grid is to be able to establish a score of the situation of handicap, only from what is observed in the daily life of the person.
This grid can be filled in by a relative, a professional from any sector, or even by the person themselves. The coefficients of the grid were decided to take into account the relative seriousness of certain disorders. They may be questioned as the grid is used. As the grid is established on a spreadsheet, the calculations are automated. The grid can be filled in at certain intervals for the same person; in this way, a variation in the mental handicap can be measured. An improvement of the person's condition, a stabilization or a deterioration can thus be objectified. Used at regular intervals, it makes it possible to establish a curve for the evaluation of the handicap situation.

Eric FEVRE, 2019

Grille d'évaluation de la situation de handicap d'origine psychique (géshop)

nom	
date	

		intensité des troubles						
		bénin (1)	léger (2)	grave (3)	sévère (4)	score	coefficient	points
1. Troubles de la volition :	a. pas de prise d'initiatives					-	**10**	-
	b. apragmatisme, impossibilité d'agir par incapacité à vouloir					-	10	-
	c. incapacité à assumer les gestes de la vie quotidienne par :							
	i. incapacité à décider					-	10	-
	ii. incapacité à agir					-	10	-
	d. incapacité à s'empêcher d'agir, actes compulsifs					-	10	-
2. Troubles de la conscience et de la vigilance :	a. non conscience des troubles					-	**9**	-
	b. absence d'expression des besoins					-	9	-
	c. non pouvoir faire une demande d'aide					-	9	-
3. Troubles de l'humeur :	a. perte d'estime de soi					-	**8**	-
	b. négativisme					-	8	-
	c. troubles dépressifs					-	8	-
	d. comportement hypomaniaque					-	8	-
4. Souffrance psychique :	a. tristesse					-	**7**	-
	b. manque de confiance en soi					-	7	-
	c. démotivation					-	7	-
	d. hypersensibilité au stress					-	7	-
	e. sentiment de dévalorisation					-	7	-
	f. recours à l'alcool ou au cannabis					-	7	-
	g. inscription silencieuse dans la pathologie					-	7	-
	h. indifférence pour sa propre vie, se laisser mourir					-	7	-
	i. idées de mort et de suicide					-	7	-
5. Troubles de la pensée :	a. lenteur ou appauvrissement de la pensée					-	**6**	-
	b. déni de la pathologie					-	6	-
	c. fuite ou incohérence des idées					-	6	-
	d. idées obsédantes					-	6	-
	e. délire					-	6	-
6. Expressions somatiques :	a. fatigabilité					-	**5**	-
	b. lenteur malgré des potentialités réelles					-	5	-
	c. agitation psychomotrice					-	5	-
	d. hypersensibilité sensorielle (visuelle, auditive)					-	5	-
	e. somatisations					-	5	-
	f. dégradation de l'état physique					-	5	-
	g. altération de l'état général					-	5	-
7. Troubles intellectuels :	a. déficit d'attention					-	**4**	-
	b. difficultés de conceptualisation et d'abstraction					-	4	-
	c. troubles de l'attention					-	4	-
	d. troubles de la mémoire					-	4	-
	e. troubles de l'orientation temporelle et spatiale					-	4	-
	f. défaut d'analyse du contexte environnemental					-	4	-
	g. incapacité à prévoir les conséquences d'un acte					-	4	-
	h. troubles du jugement					-	4	-
8. Troubles de la vie émotionnelle :	a. dérégulation émotionnelle					-	**3**	-
	b. indifférence					-	3	-
	c. anxiété					-	3	-
	d. angoisse					-	3	-
9. Troubles de la vie affective :	a. difficulté à nouer des relations					-	3	-
	b. discordance ou instabilité affective					-	3	-
	c. troubles du caractère					-	3	-
10. Troubles du comportement :	a. agitation					-	**2**	-
	b. suractivité					-	2	-
	c. agressivité					-	2	-
	d. difficulté à respecter les règles					-	2	-
	e. changements brusques d'attitude, imprévisibilité					-	2	-
	f. envahissement					-	2	-
	g. troubles du sommeil					-	3	-
	h. troubles alimentaires					-	2	-
	i. rituels					-	2	-
	j. évitements phobiques d'objets ou de situations anxiogènes					-	2	-
	k. accumulation d'objets					-	2	-
	l. incurie					-	2	-
	m. errance					-	3	-
11. Troubles de la perception :	a. hallucinations,					-	**1**	-
	b. déréalisation.					-	1	-

A discrete incapacitating syndrome of psychic origin...
Listening to those close to the peshops, to professionals and to the people concerned themselves, we have the testimony that, most of the time, the situation of disability has gradually taken hold and that prodromal signs had gone unnoticed.

I think that my Shop Evaluation Grid (Géshop) could be used to detect a progressive accumulation of clinical signs that would lead, from a certain level, to consider that the person presents a "Discrete Disabling Syndrome of Psychic Origin" (Sidop)[64] which, without preventive intervention, could lead to a shop. Sidop is therefore to be understood as a prodrome of the shop.

Perhaps the identification of a sidop would make it possible, through early intervention, to avoid the eventual occurrence of a shop.
To sum up, from this last part, we were able to study the report of the 2009 Versailles Colloquium, which brought together the actors of the time to take stock of research on mental disability and the different methods of support. An important part of this report concerned the accompaniment of peshops in housing; it referred in particular to a particular device of anticipation of the accompaniment of a SAMSAH upstream of an orientation by the MDPH.
We then took up certain passages from the Charzat report, in particular the descriptions of behaviours that characterise psychological disability, and the social repercussions of these, particularly in daily life and especially in housing.
Then we searched in other sources, to refine the perception of the shops on a daily basis, by relatives, professionals and some researchers. We were thus able to see a very large number of situations in which peshops find themselves in difficulty, personally and in their relationship with others.
I put aside the sociological aspects of the shops, and retained the psychological characteristics. So I drew up a *clinical picture of the shops*.

From this table, I made a Grid for the *evaluation of the situation of handicap of psychic origin* (Géshop) which allows to objectify a situation of handicap and even to measure the psychic handicap. Used at some interval, it can measure a variation of the situation of handicap.

The evaluation grid can also be used to highlight a prodromal situation in the shop, namely a *discrete incapacitating syndrome of psychic origin* (sidop).

---

[64] The syndrome is about us

Conclusion

Contrary to a common representation of mental disability as a harmful social consequence of psychiatric illness, psychologists consider mental disability as the result of individual mental fragility in a hostile environment, or at least with little understanding of the manifestations of mental suffering.
Their representation of the situation of disability of psychological origin allows us to apprehend people in this situation as full-fledged citizens, actors of their life course, to whom psychologists provide support that can go as far as the setting up of psychotherapy, at home if necessary; indeed, a first-line intervention by clinical psychologists at home allows us to meet people in great psychological suffering, in denial and therefore without demand.

Even if François Chapireau (2014) indicates that mental disability is a "social construction of a new, specifically French disorder", that "this new French notion" is "difficult to translate into a foreign language", the situation of disability of mental origin is indeed a daily reality that psychologists working in the home are confronted with.

A "collaborative research platform on mental health and mental disability" was set up in 2015 in the Paris Region. Under the aegis of the Regional Health Agency (ARS), it is led by the Ville-Évrard public mental health establishment, which is at the initiative[65]. Among the themes to be researched, we note that the reception, information, evaluation and orientation systems are mentioned.
More recently, on 2 December 2016, the Inter-ministerial Committee on Disability (CIH) identified fourteen priority actions to support the autonomy of people with disabilities. These include: "Taking better account of mental disability".

However, research on psychic disability still seems to be shy, especially in psychology. Thus Marie-Christine Hardy-Baylé (2015) has produced a report that has aroused great interest among those involved in mental handicap; however, we note, once again, that mental handicap is understood as "undertended by a schizophrenic disorder".

---

[65] http://www.eps-ville-evrard.fr/enseignement-recherche/recherche-handicap-psychique-ursm-hp/

Psychic disability, which we now call *Situation of disability of psychic origin (shop),* has inherited, in the course of this work, a new definition, which does not refer to a psychiatric illness.
At its origin, we can assume a *psychic incapacitating syndrome (sidop)* that specialized teams (ESEHP) could diagnose by means of the clinical picture that we propose to them.
This clinical picture could also be disseminated for early diagnosis with a view to prevention. In this way, we could avoid that certain vulnerable people with a singular psychic fragility become *people in a situation of psychic handicap (peshop).*

We were interested in peshops, that is to say, people who are already in a situation of disability. We indicated a possible psychic fragility of these people, but we did not wonder about what could be prodromic signs of the shop.

However, we have indicated the probability of a Discrete Psychic Disability Syndrome (sidop) which could indicate the fragility of a person who, following a traumatic event, could decompensate towards a situation of disability of psychic origin.

Thus, the field of research on the origin of the situation of disability of psychic origin is still open.

To contact me: fevre44eric@gmail.com or on LinkedIn.

Bibliography

Association Française de Psychiatrie; Comité d'Action Syndical de la Psychiatrie; Conférence nationale des Présidents; Fédération d'aide à la Santé Mentale Croix-Marine; Fédération Nationale des associations d'(EX)Patients-Psy; Fédération Française de Psychiatrie; Ligue Française pour la Santé Mentale; UNAFAM. 2001. *Le Livre Blanc des partenaires de Santé Mentale France, pour une association d'usagers de la psychiatrie, de soignants et de responsables de social dans la cité,* Paris, Editions de Santé.

BAILLON, Georges. 2009. *Les usagers au secours de la psychiatrie. La parole retrouvée*, Toulouse, érès

Baptiste, René. 2005. *Reconnaitre le handicap psychique ; développer et améliorer la réinsertion sociale et professionnelle*, L'essentiel, Lyon, Chronique sociale

Béliard, Aude; Eideliman, Jean-Sébastien. 2009. Aux frontières du handicap psychique: genèse et usage des catégories médico-administratives, *Revue française des affaires sociales,* N° 162, pp. 99-116, Paris, La Documentation française.

BELIO, Christian. 2012. *Handicap, cognition and representations*, Bordeaux, Université Bordeaux Segalen.

BEULNE, Thierry; Zribi, Gérard (eds.). 2009. *Les handicaps psychiques, Concepts, approches, pratiques,* Rennes, Presses de l'EHESP

BLOCH-LAINE, François. 1969. *Étude du problème général de l'inadaptation des personnes handicapées*, Paris, La Documentation française.

BOUCHERAT-HUE, Valérie; Peretti, Pascale. 2012. Du handicap revisité au handicap psychique : un nouveau concept qui pourrait bien faire date ?, *Annales Médico-Psychologiques,* 170(9), Issy-les-Moulineaux, Elsevier-Masson

BOUCHERAT-HUE, Valerie. 2012. Le " péripsychotique " dans les cliniques interstitielles de l'excitation et de l'inhibition somato-psychique, *Recherches en psychanalyse,* n° 13, pp. 32-42, Paris, Université Paris 7

BOUCHERAT-HUE, Valerie. 2013. "From the deformed to the shapeless. Le travail du contre-transfert corporel dans la cure d'un jeune homme "péripsychotique" souffrant d'un handicap "somato-psychique" ", *Champ psychosomatique,* " Le corps de l'analyste ", n° 63, pp. 75-88, Bègles, L'esprit du temps

BOUCHERAT-HUE, Valerie. 2016. Introduction. Pour une approche " somato-psychique " du handicap en psychiatrie, in V. BOUCHERAT-HUE, D. LEGUAY, B. Pachoud, A. PLAGNOL and F. WEBER, *Handicap psychique : questions vives,* pp. 315-324, Toulouse, érès

BOUCHERAT-HUE, Valerie; Brother ARTINIAN, Chantal. 2016. Disability and neurotic disorders. L'expérience sensorielle de la "(re)médiation corporo-psychique, in V. BOUCHERAT-HUE, D. LEGUAY, B. Pachoud, A. PLAGNOL and F. WEBER, *Handicap psychique : questions vives,* pp. 351-365, Toulouse, érès

Bolt, Yann; GAYTON, Roger. 2009. Assessing Psychic Disability and Compensation Needs. Presentation of an experimentation of ESEHPs. R. GAYTON and Y. Boulon, in J. DELBECK and F. WEBER (coordinated by), *Handicap psychique et vie quotidienne,* Revue française des affaires sociales, Paris, La Documentation française.

Boulon, Yann; DESCHAMPS, Valérie. 2009. Situation de handicap psychique, de l'évaluation à la compensation, expérimentation des ESEHP (équipes spécialisées d'évaluation du handicap psychique), in Galaxie, CNSA, *Rapport d'étude,* www.reseau-galaxie.fr

Brossard, Baptiste.; WEBER, Florence. 2016. "Folie et société: ce qu'apporte et ce que manque la question du handicap, in V. BOUCHERAT-HUE, D. LEGUAY, B. Pachoud, A. PLAGNOL and F. WEBER, *Handicap psychique : questions vives,* pp.173-191, Toulouse, érès.

CASELLAS-MENIERE, Marie-France. 2006. La prestation de compensation appliquée au handicap psychique, UNAFAM, Dossier MDPH, *Un autre regard,* Revue de liaison trimestrielle de l'UNAFAM, n° 2-2006, Paris, Unafam

Cevasco, Rithee. 1984. In loco, in altero, on the distinction between neurosis and psychosis, *Analytica volume 37*, pp. 50-51, Paris, Navarin éditeur.

CHAPIREAU, François. 2014. Le handicap psychique : la construction sociale d'un nouveau trouble spécifiquement français, *Socio-logos [Online], 9 | 2014, online* April 17, 2014, accessed November 04, 2016, http://socio-logos.revues.org/2824

ICD 10, 1994. International Classification of Mental and Behavioural Disorders, Diagnostic Criteria for Research, *ICD 10 / CIM 10,* World Health Organization, Paris, Masson.

CNSA. 2008. *Guide to Assessing the Compensation Needs of Persons with Disabilities (GEVA),* http://www.cnsa.fr/compensation-de-la-perte-dautonomie-du-projet-de-vie-a-la-compensation/levaluation-des-besoins/le-geva.

CNSA. 2013. *Eligibility guide for decisions made in Departmental Houses for the Disabled*, www.cnsa.fr.

Collège National des Universitaires en Psychiatrie (CNUP); Association pour l'Enseignement de la Sémiologie Psychiatrique (AESP); Collège National Universitaires des Enseignants en Addictologie (CUNEA). 2014. *Psychiatry and addictology reference system. Adult Psychiatry. Child and Adolescent Psychiatry. Addictology*, Tours, Presses Universitaires François Rabelais

DE GROEF Johan. 2009. Le double diagnostic : une affaire louche ?, in BEULNE Thierry, Zribi Gérard, under the direction of, *Les handicaps psychiques, Concepts, approches, pratiques,* pp. 25-40, Rennes, Presses de l'EHESP.

DELEU, Guy. 2015. Where Psychiatric Rehabilitation Leads Us, Marchienne-au-Pont, Éditions Socrate Promarex

DEMAILLY, Lise. 2012. "La santé mentale," *Actualités Sociales hebdomadaires,* No. 2778, p. 32, Paris, Info6tm.

Research, Studies, Evaluation and Statistics Directorate (Dress). 2010. *Disability Health Survey, 2008-2009. www.*drees.sante.gouv.fr/les-enquetes-handicap-sante,4267.html

ESPING-ANDERSEN, Gøsta. 1990. *Les trois mondes de l'État-providence,* Paris, Presses Universitaires de France.

ESQUIROL, Étienne. 1838. *Des maladies mentales considérées sous le rapport médical, hygiénique et médico-légal,* Paris, Bailiwick.

FALISSARD, Bernard. 2016. Commentary. Disability and mental illness: a story of a tension that has not yet been resolved, in V. BOUCHERAT-HUE, D. LEGUAY, B. Pachoud, A. PLAGNOL and F. WEBER, *Handicap psychique : questions vives*, pp. 87-89, Toulouse, érès

Faure, Jean-Louis. 1979. Psychose, in Robert LAFON *Vocabulaire de psychopédagogie et de psychiatrie de l'enfant,* p. 879, Paris, PUF.

Fèvre, Eric. 2017. *Handicap psychique et exclusion sociale : place des phénomènes cliniques et psychopathologiques dans les risques d'expulsion d'un logement*, doctoral thesis in psychology, University of Angers, http://www.theses.fr/2017ANGE0047

FOUCHER, J.R. (2008). Cognitive neuropsychology's approach to schizophrenia. Unpublished paper,
quoted by Isabelle OFFERLIN-MEYER, 2012, in *Handicap psychique et schizophrénie : évaluation et remédiation cognitive des troubles mnésiques impliqués dans les difficultés de la vie quotidienne et/ou professionnelle des patients*, doctoral thesis in psychology, University of Strasbourg

Fougeyrollas, Patrick. 1986. Processes of Disability Production and the Struggle for the Autonomy of Persons with Disabilities, *Anthropology and Societies*, vol. 10, No. 2 pp. 183-186, http://id.eudit;org/iderudit/OO6357ar

Fougeyrollas, Patrick. 1998. *Réseau international sur le processus de production de handicap, Classification québécoise - Processus de production du handicap,* Lac Saint-Charles, Québec, RIPPH-SCCIDIH.

GALAXY; CNSA. 2009. *Situation de handicap psychique, De l'évaluation à la compensation, Expérimentation des ESEHP (Equipes Spécialisées d'Evaluation du Handicap Psychique),* Rapport d'étude, www.reseau-galaxie.fr

GIORDANO, Gaëlle. 2016. Le handicap psychique des adultes à l'épreuve de l'action publique, in V. BOUCHERAT-HUE, D. LEGUAY, B. PACHOUD, A. PLAGNOL and F. WEBER, *Handicap psychique : questions vives*, pp. 29-44, Toulouse, érès

Giraud-Baro, Elizabeth. 2016. Psychic disability: health care. La réhabilitation psychosociale dans son versant sanitaire, in V. BOUCHERAT-HUE, D. LEGUAY, B. Pachoud, A. PLAGNOL and F. WEBER, *Handicap psychique : questions vives,* pp. 247-257, Toulouse, érès

GREACEN, Tim. 2016. Commentary. Beyond Psychic Disability: Recovery and Valuing the Experience of Psychic Illness, in V. Boucherat-Hue, D. Leguay, B. Pachoud, A. Plagnol and F. Weber. *Handicap psychique : questions vives*, Toulouse, érès.

HAMONET, Claude. 2010. *Les personnes en situation de handicap*, Que sais-je? 6th edition, Paris, PUF

HARDY-BAYLE, Marie-Christine. 2015. *Evidence for improving the care and life course of people with mental retardation due to schizophrenic disorder*, http://crehpsy-documentation.fr/opac/doc_num.php?explnum_id=323

HENCKES, Nicolas. 2009. Psychiatrists and Psychic Disability. De l'après-guerre aux années 1980, *Revue française des affaires sociales,* vol. 1, n° 1-2, pp. 25-40, Paris, La Documentation française

HENCKES, Nicolas. 2011. *La politique du handicap psychique, familles, psychiatres et État face à la chronicité des maladies mentales, des années 1960 aux années 1980,* rapport DREES/MIRE, Paris, Ministère des solidarités et de la famille

General Inspectorate of Social Affairs. 2011. *La prise en charge du handicap psychique,* Rapport tome 1, s, RM2011-133P, Paris, Ministry of Social Affairs.

JAEGER, Marcel (under the direction of). 2003. *Guide de la législation en droit social*, Paris, Dunod.

KRISTEVA, Julia. 2002. *Letter to the President of the Republic*, Paris, Fayard.

LACAN, Jacques. 1955. *Les Psychoses*, Le séminaire (1955-1956), book III, text by Jacques-Alain MILLER, 1981, Paris, Le Seuil.

LACAN, Jacques. 1966. Écrits, Paris, Le Seuil

LACAN, Jacques. 2001. Other writings, Paris, Le Seuil

THE ROY-HATALA, Claire. 2009. Les handicaps psychiques : un nouveau enjeu pour les entreprises ou une nouvelle façon de traiter un problème ancien ? in BEULNÉ Thierry, ZRIBI Gérard (sous la direction de), *Les handicaps psychiques, Concepts, approches, pratiques,* pp. 107-115, Rennes, Presses de l'EHESP

Lelièvre, Jean. 2006. *L'enfant inefficient intellectuel*, Amphi psychologie, Paris, Bréal.

LIBERMAN, Roman. 2011. *Handicap et maladie mentale*, Que sais-je, 8ème édition, Paris, PUF

MALEVAL, Jean-Claude. 2011. *Logique du délire*, Rennes, Presses Universitaires de Rennes.

MISES, Roger; QUEMADA, Nicole 1994. *Classification of disabilities in child and adolescent psychiatry: disabilities, disadvantages and impact on the quality of family life,* Psychiatric Information, 70(5), pp. 453-462, Nanterre, John Libbey Eurotex.

MOREAU, Delphine. 2010. What do we do when we nominate? The psychic handicap facing the figures of "madness" and mental illness, *Annales médico-psychologiques*, vol. 168, n° 10, p. 770-772, Issy-les-Moulineaux, Elsevier-Masson.

MOUILLIE, Jean-Marc; LEFEVRE, Céline; VISIER, Laurent (eds.). 2010. *Médecine et sciences humaines, manuel pour les études médicales,* collection Médecine et sciences humaines, Paris, Les Belles Lettres

MULLER, Sebastian. 2011. *Comprendre le handicap psychique, éléments théoriques, analyses de cas,* Nimes, Champ social éditions

OETH; Living Emergence. 2011. *Psychic disability and employment, if we talked about it,* https://www.defi-metiers.fr/sites/default/files/users/379/oeth_-_handicap_psychique_et_emploi.pdf

Pachoud, Bernard; PLAGNOL, Arnaud. 2016. La perspective du rétablissement: sortir du handicap psychique plutôt qu'en attendre la compensation, in V. BOUCHERAT-HUE, D. LEGUAY, B. Pachoud, A. PLAGNOL and F. WEBER, *Handicap psychique : questions vives,* pp. 103-123, Toulouse, France, érès.

PAINTER, Carole. 2010. What support services for people with disabilities of psychological origin? Cedias, social museum, CREAHI Ile-de-France, DREES-MiRe and CNSA, in collaboration with the DGAS, GIS-IRESP and UNAFAM, *2008 Research Programme "Psychic Disability, Autonomy, Social Life", Partial Report,* Paris, Ministry of Solidarity and the Family.

PAINTER, Carole. 2010. What support services for people with psychic disabilities? Cedias, social museum, CREAHI Ile-de-France, DREES-MiRe and CNSA, in collaboration with the DGAS, GIS-IRESP and UNAFAM, *2008 Research Programme "Psychic disability, autonomy, social life", Summary,* Paris, Unafam.

Pivin, Michèle. 2006. Une réponse aux attentes des personnes handicapées psychiques ?, UNAFAM, Dossier MDPH, *Un autre regard,* Revue de liaison trimestrielle de l'UNAFAM, No. 2-2006, Paris, Unafam.

PLAGNOL, Arnaud; Pachoud, Bernard. 2016. Functional capacity and functioning in real-life situations, in V. BOUCHERAT-HUE, D. LEGUAY, B. Pachoud, A. PLAGNOL and F. WEBER, *Handicap psychique : questions vives,*pp. 193-214, Toulouse, érès

POSTEL, Jacques. 1972. *De la folie,* Privât, coll. Rhadamanthe 1999, Paris, L'Harmattan.

Prouteau, Antoinette; Koleck, Michèle; BELIO, Christian; BONILLA-GUERRERO, Julien; DAYRE, Emmanuelle, DESTAILLATS, Jean-Marc; MAZAUX, Jean-Michel. 2016. Apprehending situations of psychic handicap; interests and limits of evaluation methods, in V. BOUCHERAT-HUE, D. LEGUAY, B. Pachoud, A. PLAGNOL and F. WEBER, *Handicap psychique : questions vives,* pp. 125-142, Toulouse, érès

REY, Alain (Ed.). 2016. *Dictionnaire Historique de la langue française.* Paris: Le Robert.

REY, Alain; REY-DEBOVE, Josette (eds.). 2014. *Le Petit Robert*, Paris, Le Robert

FUNNY, Juan. 2001. *Lire le délire, aliénisme, rhétorique et littérature en France au XIXe siècle,* Paris, Fayard.

ROMAN, Diane (under the direction of). 2012. *Social rights, between human rights and social policies. Which holders for which rights?* Paris, LGDJ

ROUSSEL, Pascale; VELCHE, Dominique. 2011. "La participation sociale des personnes présentant un handicap psychique : effet de rhétorique ou perspective nouvelle", IRESP/EHESP report, Rennes, Presses de l'EHESP.

ROUSSEL, Pascale; GIORDANO, Gaëlle; CUENOT, Marie. 2014. De la difficulté d'estimer le handicap psychique dans une enquête en population générale. L'exemple de l'enquête handicap-santé, *Bulletin Épidémiologique Hebdomadaire,* n° 11, pp. 184-191, Saint-Maurice, Santé publique France

SARFATY, Jacques. 2009. Handicaps psychiques ?, in T. BEULNE, G. Zribi (eds.), *Les handicaps psychiques ; Concepts, approches, pratiques,* pp. 41-43, Rennes, Presses de l'EHESP

STIKER, Henri-Jacques. 1996. *Corps infirmes et société*, Paris, Dunod.

STIKER, Henri-Jacques. 2009. *The metamorphosis of disability from 1970 to the present day. Soi-même avec les autres,* Collection handicap vieillissement société, Grenoble, PUG

STIKER, Henri-Jacques; PUIG, José; HUET, Olivier. 2009. *Handicap et accompagnement; nouvelles attentes, nouvelles pratiques,* Paris, Dunod.

Swain, Gladys. 1977. *Le sujet de la folie : naissance de la psychiatrie,* Rhadamanthe, Toulouse, Privât

Szasz, Thomas. 1975. *Le Mythe de la maladie mentale,* Paris, Payot.

UNAFAM; CNSA; UNA. 2008. *L'accueil et l'accompagnement des personnes en situation de handicap psychique dans le cadre de l'application de la loi pour l'égalité des droits et des chances, la participation et la citoyenneté des personnes handicapées,* Paris, Unafam

Vaginay, Denis. 2006. *Discovering Intellectual Disabilities*, Toulouse, France.

VEIL, Claude. 1968. *Handicap et société*, Paris, Flammarion.

WEBER, Florence. 2011. *Handicap et dépendance, drames humains, enjeux politiques,* collection du CEPREMAP, Paris, Éditions rue d'Ulm.

WEBER, Florence. 2016. Introduction; Mental, Cognitive or Psychic; Qualifying Disability for Professional Care, in V. BOUCHERAT-HUE, D. LEGUAY, B. Pachoud, A. PLAGNOL and F. WEBER, *Handicap psychique : questions vives,* pp. 21-27, Toulouse, érès

Zribi, Gérard. 2009. Les handicaps psychiques : état des lieux et problématique, in BEULNE Thierry, Zribi Gérard (eds.), *Les handicaps psychiques, Concepts, approches, pratiques,* pp. 13-23, Rennes, Presses de l'EHESP.

Table of Contents

Printed in Great Britain
by Amazon

82585659R00079